© D. C. Thomson & Co., Ltd., 1967.

This book was presented to

_____

*by*_____

*on*_____

Diana

FOR GIRLS

Printed and Published by D. C. Thomson & Co., Ltd.,
Dundee and London.

THE GIRLS FROM N.O.O.D.L.E.S.

GALE PRICE and Nicola Main are two agents from N.O.O.D.L.E.S. (National Organisation for Order, Discipline and Law Enforcement in Schools). High-speed rocket-propelled bikes take the girls swiftly to the ruined abbey which conceals N.O.O.D.L.E.S. headquarters.

The girls reported to Miss Z, head of the organisation, who showed them some film slides.

THIS IS DOWNDALE PRIVATE SCHOOL— THE MOST EXCLUSIVE IN THE COUNTRY. BUT LATELY THE SCHOOL IS BEING TERRORISED— PUPILS AND STAFF ARE LEAVING AT AN ALARMING RATE. YOU WILL INVESTIGATE.

Before leaving, Gale and Nicola called at the gadget department for some special equipment.

YOU'LL FIND A USE FOR MOST OF THESE ON YOUR LATEST ASSIGNMENT. GOOD LUCK!

And so, the following evening, the two girls, posing as new pupils, arrived at Downdale.

GOLLY—IT'S LIKE A STATELY HOME. WHAT AN ENTRANCE—

LOOK OUT, GALE!

Suddenly, one of the carved stone eagles on the gate post toppled off and fell towards Gale.

But quick action by Nicola saved Gale as the eagle crashed to the ground, missing the girls by inches.

Immediately the girls searched the foliage by the gate post.

NOBODY THERE, GALE. BUT I'M NOT SO SURE THAT EAGLE FELL BY ACCIDENT. WE MUST WATCH OUR STEP.

Once inside the school, Miss Smithers, the headmistress, showed Gale and Nicola to their dormitory.

I'M SO GLAD YOU'VE ARRIVED—MISS Z AND I ARE OLD FRIENDS. I HOPE YOU CAN FIND OUT WHO IS TERRORISING MY SCHOOL.

Later that night both girls were awakened by a violent, shuddering sensation.

WHAT ON EARTH IS GOING ON? THE SCHOOL IS SHAKING LIKE A JELLY.

The girls looked out of the window.

IT'S A TRAIN. I DIDN'T REALISE THE LINE RAN SO CLOSE TO THE SCHOOL. CAN'T SEE US GETTING MUCH SLEEP TILL WE GET USED TO THE RACKET!

Next day, Gale and Nicola joined the other pupils at the outdoor swimming pool.

LET'S TAKE A DIP, GALE. MIGHT AS WELL ENJOY OURSELVES WHILE WE CAN.

But no sooner had the girls dived into the pool, than there was a mad scramble to get out again.

MY EYES— THEY'RE SMARTING—

I CAN HARDLY SEE.

WHAT HAPPENED, GALE? OH! MY EYES! IT'S AS IF SOMEONE HAD THROWN PEPPER INTO THEM.

SOMEBODY HAS PUT AN OVERDOSE OF CHLORINE IN THE FRESH WATER. WE'RE ALL HALF-BLINDED.

Miss Smithers arrived to comfort the distressed girls—but some of them wouldn't be comforted.

LET'S GET OUT OF THIS PLACE.

I'M LEAVING THIS SCHOOL! IT'S HORRID— WAIT TILL I TELL MY FATHER!

That afternoon, in the gym, Nicola did a spot of rope climbing, while Gale and another girl got out the school trampoline.

Without warning, Nicola's rope snapped and she went plunging down —

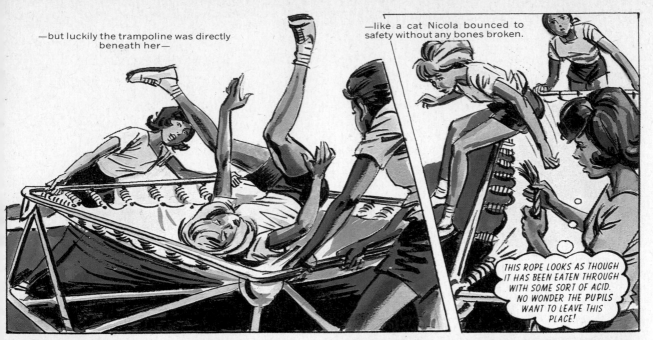

—but luckily the trampoline was directly beneath her—

—like a cat Nicola bounced to safety without any bones broken.

THIS ROPE LOOKS AS THOUGH IT HAS BEEN EATEN THROUGH WITH SOME SORT OF ACID. NO WONDER THE PUPILS WANT TO LEAVE THIS PLACE!

That night, the girls put on their special black suits to search the sleeping school. Nicola carried an instrument like a geiger counter which was designed to amplify the slightest sound.

The sound detector began to glow red as Nicola and Gale approached a suit of armour in the hallway.

SSSH, GALE— IT'S PICKED UP A SOUND COMING FROM THE ARMOUR.

Gale got quite a fright when she lifted the visor of the armour and a voice spoke—

EVERYTHING IS GOING AS PLANNED.

The girls carefully moved the armour to reveal an opening in the wall behind.

IT LOOKS LIKE SOME SORT OF SECRET PASSAGE. THE VOICE CAME FROM IN THERE I'LL BET.

Cautiously, they entered the secret passage—

LOOK, FOOTPRINTS IN THE DUST LEADING TO THAT TRAP-DOOR.

Through the open trapdoor, Gale and Nicola saw a group of men below.

STOP THE MIDNIGHT MAIL TRAIN TOMORROW NIGHT. WE'VE GOT THE KIDS AND STAFF SO SCARED THEY WON'T DARE GET OUT OF BED. AFTER THE ROBBERY WE COME BACK HERE TO SHARE OUT—TWO MILLION POUNDS —SOME HAUL, EH?

Gently, Nicola closed the trapdoor.

SO THAT'S IT! A GANG OF TRAIN ROBBERS ARE USING THE SCHOOL AS THEIR HEADQUARTERS TILL THEY ROB THE MAIL TRAIN. WE'VE GOT TO STOP THEM.

Later, Gale contacted Miss Z on her powder compact radio.

CALLING MISS Z! WE'VE FOUND OUT WHO IS TERRORISING THE SCHOOL—

At N.O.O.D.L.E.S. head-quarters, Miss Z took careful note of Gale's report.

WELL DONE— JUST KEEP A CLOSE EYE ON THEM AND LEAVE THE REST TO ME. I'LL BE IN TOUCH WITH YOU.

It was lashing rain and blowing a gale the next night as the midnight mail train thundered towards the robbers' trap.

The robbers had already left the school and were making for the railway line—but, as instructed, Gale and Nicola were keeping a very close watch on them.

The gang fixed explosives to various points along the track.

THESE ARE LIKE DETONATORS. WHEN THE TRAIN HITS THEM THEY'LL GO OFF, AND THE DRIVER WILL STOP, THINKING IT'S A WARNING OF DANGER ON THE TRACK AHEAD.

At last the midnight mail appeared. The engine exploded the detonators and the driver brought the train screeching to a halt.

Then the gang went into action.

THIS IS THE MAIL COACH, BOSS.

BACK UP AND KEEP QUIET—THAT WAY NO ONE WILL GET HURT.

But outside, Gale and Nicola took a hand in things. First, they put the look-outs out of action—

—then they headed for the mail coach.

COME ON, NICOLA. THIS IS WHAT MISS Z TOLD US TO DO.

The robbers were opening the mail sacks when Gale and Nicola surprised them.

DON'T MOVE ANOTHER INCH, WHOEVER YOU ARE.

Surprise number two came when the mail sacks sprang open and out popped a group of N.O.O.D.L.E.S. agents.

THE GAME'S UP. DROP YOUR GUNS.

And so the gang were rounded up.

WELL DONE, GALE AND NICOLA. YOU PLAYED A VERY IMPORTANT PART IN THE CAPTURE OF THESE MEN. THEY WON'T BE ROBBING ANY MORE TRAINS FOR A LONG, LONG TIME.

Some days later in Miss "Z's" study at N.O.O.D.L.E.S. headquarters.

BY THE WAY, GIRLS—DOWNDALE IS BACK IN BUSINESS AGAIN— MORE PUPILS THAN THEY CAN COPE WITH—THANKS TO YOU AND THE PUBLICITY THEY GOT.

SPYLAND GAMES

SPIES and secret agents in fact and fiction always have a host of weird and wonderful gadgets and tricky gimmicks to help them outwit the "baddies." Here are just a few such interesting gadgets:—

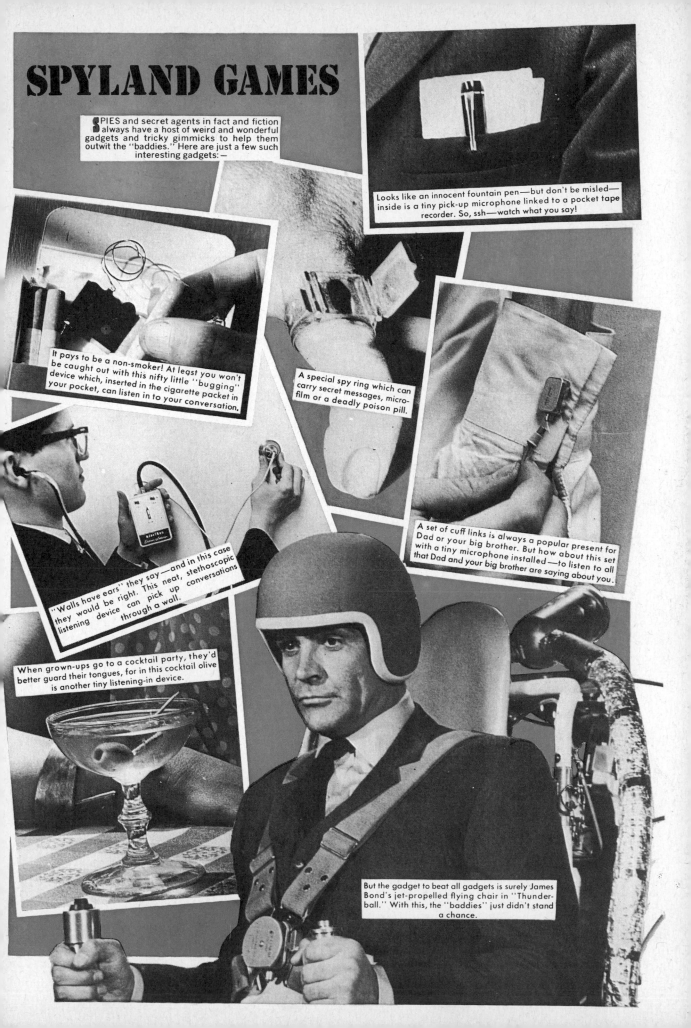

Looks like an innocent fountain pen—but don't be misled—inside is a tiny pick-up microphone linked to a pocket tape recorder. So, ssh—watch what you say!

It pays to be a non-smoker! At least you won't be caught out with this nifty little "bugging" device which, inserted in the cigarette packet in your pocket, can listen in to your conversation.

A special spy ring which can carry secret messages, microfilm or a deadly poison pill.

A set of cuff links is always a popular present for Dad or your big brother. But how about this set with a tiny microphone installed—to listen to all that Dad and your big brother are saying about you.

"Walls have ears" they say—and in this case they would be right. This neat, stethoscopic listening device can pick up conversations through a wall.

When grown-ups go to a cocktail party, they'd better guard their tongues, for in this cocktail olive is another tiny listening-in device.

But the gadget to beat all gadgets is surely James Bond's jet-propelled flying chair in "Thunderball." With this, the "baddies" just didn't stand a chance.

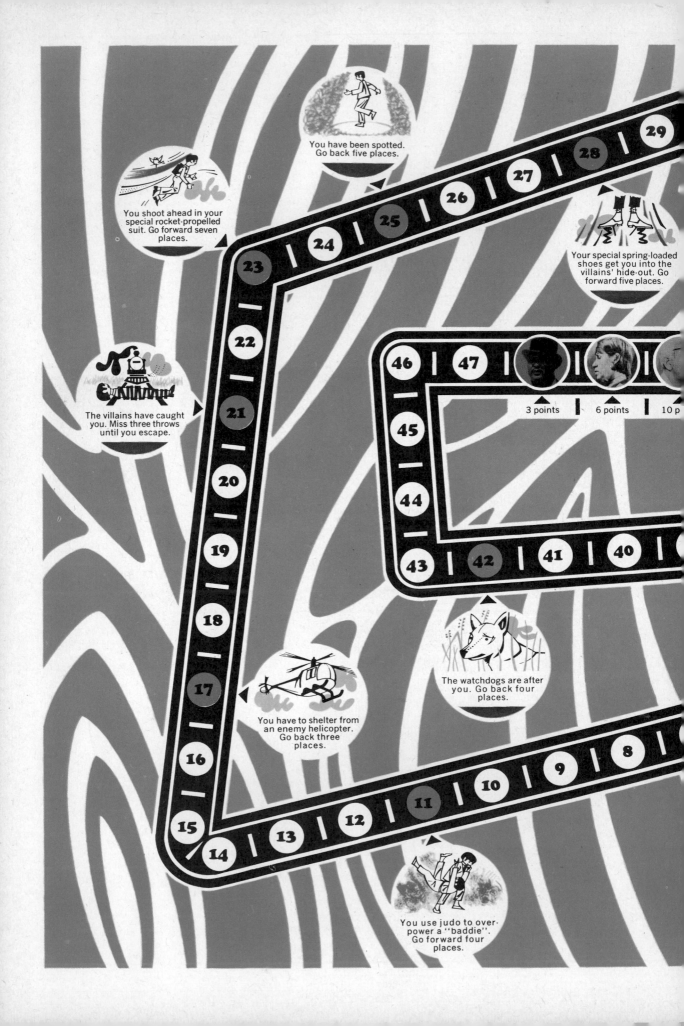

THE SECRET AGENT GAME
(– or catch yourself a villain)

Six can play this exciting 'secret agent' game. All you need is a dice and six discs of cardboard.

First, find yourself photographs of the agents shown below, cut them out and paste them on to pieces of cardboard.

Now each player selects her favourite secret agent—ready to set off after the villains.

throw a six to start here

You will see three well-known villains at the end of the chase — each one carrying a score in points. Just follow the rules and when you land on a villain, that is the end of the round, and it's back to the beginning to start again — no matter where the other players are.

Keep a note of your 'villains' points, and at the end of five rounds the player with the highest number of points is Top Secret Agent.

The villains have sabotaged your snorkel. Go back eight places.

Your gun is out of ammunition. Reload — throw a six to start again.

Your car is blown up! Go back two places.

LUCKY PENNY CROSSES SWORDS WITH ADAM ADAMANT

—but only to find the answers to some interesting questions!

Where were you born?
In the centre of London town.

What were some of your favourite subjects at school?
English language and French. Although with school—I liked the life but not the lessons.

What are your hobbies?
Eating with my friends. Riding in the country.

As "Adam Adamant" you originally existed in Victorian times—would you liked to have lived then? If not—which century would you choose to live in?
No—I'm not very keen on the Victorian era, or any other era—except this one. I think the 20th century is quite the best time because there's plenty of freedom and opportunities for every single person.

How did you get the part of "Adam Adamant"?
This instance it was very simple and straightforward—no audition with 600 other chaps. Two people picked me—Sidney Newman, the head of the TV Drama Department, and the producer, Miss Verity Lambert. Sidney Newman had seen me in a Frances Durbridge serial and retorted solemnly, "That's the man for Adam." And when Verity saw me face to face, she agreed that I was "just the fella."

What roles would you most like to play?
There are a few. Iago in "Othello." Professor Higgins in what was "Pygmalion" and is now "My Fair Lady." Almost any role in Chekhov's plays.

Also Algernon or Earnest in Oscar Wilde's "The Importance of Being Earnest." And I've one great passion—to be a dame in pantomime.

If you weren't an actor—what would you choose to do for a living?
I'd be a farmer—genuinely I think it's a marvellous life, and the people—you know the farming crowd—are so nice.

What type of music do you most enjoy?
I love Mozart and Verdi, in fact nearly all music—although I'm not mad on pop.

Who is your favourite—male and female—film star?
For the male—Paul Newman definitely. What a marvellous, witty actor. And the female—Julie Christie. She's such a good actress and so typical of this generation in every way—looks, spirit, personality—the lot.

If you could treat yourself to one thing at this moment—what would it be?
A super lunch with you. Something really marvellous at one of those "olde Englishe" inns in the heart of the country—possibly Berkshire. Those places always have a fantastic atmosphere.

What are your favourite colours?
Deep plushy red—like the sumptuous shade of the Covent Garden curtains. I like combinations of colours, too, like those in the paintings by El Greco.

What is your favourite food?
I like—spare ribs, cold meats, cold shrimps, Scotch eggs.

If you were going round the world in 80 days—whom would you take for company? No relatives allowed.
I'd take Jane Austen. It would be staggering to hear her views of the world and society in this century. I also like her marvellous sense of wit. And I believe she was a very pretty woman as well—cool and elegant, charming and feminine. Yes, she'd suit me perfectly.

What has been one of your most unforgettable moments?
Well, this is an incident which, for some unknown reason, I cannot blot out of my memory. Goodness only knows why, because it's very unimportant. When I was at prep school, our form put on some sort of fairy-tale play at the end of term—and I played a wicked policeman. At one point, I had to prick myself on a bush and jump about like a Jack-in-the-Box. And when I did this at the performance, all the little boys howled with laughter and clapped and egged me on to do it again and again. After the show, lots of my pals came up and told me how funny I'd looked and could I show them how to do it. I remember, even now, how terribly important and popular and incredibly happy I felt at that moment.

What would you most like to achieve in the future?
I'd like to lead a really full life—I hope that doesn't sound like a chairman at the annual board meeting. But, you know—not to have wasted myself as a person or waste opportunities in my career. There are a great many things which interest me—and I'd like to have a go at as many of them as possible.

STARR
OF WONDERLAND

ON his huge estate, millionaire Sir Arnold Starr has created a Wonderland — a place full of interest and surprises, especially for children.

Diana, his daughter, is Wonderland's Flying Messenger. In a marvellous rocket suit, she patrols the whole area, on the look-out for trouble. And there's usually some to be found!

One day Diana watched a little girl come in at the main gate.

COULD WE PLEASE GO TO NURSERY RHYME LAND, GREAT-AUNT?

WE SHALL NOT WASTE OUR TIME WITH SUCH NONSENSE. WE SHALL VISIT THE TOWER OF LONDON REPLICA, AND LEARN SOMETHING OF OUR NATION'S GLORIOUS PAST.

GOLLY, I DON'T THINK THAT LITTLE GIRL WILL ENJOY HER VISIT TO WONDERLAND VERY MUCH.

But Diana had more to do than worry about one little girl. There was her routine afternoon patrol to do.

As she went her rounds, Diana received a mid-air call for help over her two-way radio.

MISS DIANA...CALLING MISS DIANA. PLEASE COME TO TOWER OF LONDON...PROBLEM OF LOST CHILD...

ON MY WAY!

MALLARD'S Morning

THEY glided in line astern, seven fledgeling mallards, their feathers soft as down, six of them identical in size and chevron markings.

The seventh was The Odd One. Smaller than the rest, his colouring paler, he looked as if he had been in the wash too often.

Ahead of them sailed their plump mother, an alert expression in her eyes as she led her freshly-hatched brood upstream towards the backwater, where they could count on a breakfast of duckweed and water insects.

A Royal family of cygnets swept by, the parents moving with slow, regal grace, a satiny sheen on their white plumage, guarding the little grey balls of fluff that would, before long, turn into swans like themselves.

The young mallards watched them go by without envy, accepting the fact that they themselves were fatherless. One parent was better than none, and they trusted their mother to see they came to no harm, for instinct told them that dangers, as yet unknown, might lurk in wait for the unprotected.

The Odd One knew it wasn't easy to tell who were your friends and who your enemies.

Rounding a bend they came to a quieter channel, where the water was calm and shallow. Bungalows could be seen beyond the willows, with lawns sloping down to landing stages where punts and skiffs were moored.

In one of the boats reclined a Siamese cat. She glanced at the ducklings, and The Odd One shivered with apprehension, wondering if this large furry creature could be an enemy.

Her eyes watched the visitors' every move, but she made no move to attack them.

The mallard family sailed over to a small inlet on the other side, a bird sanctuary where trees and vegetation grew.

They had just commenced their breakfast of duckweed when, from the bungalow opposite, a dog emerged and came bounding across the lawn.

A Yorkshire terrier, he was little more than a puppy, with a silky sheen on his honey-coloured coat, and sharp, intelligent brown eyes fringed with long tendrils of fur.

The Siamese hissed at him and, mistaking this for an invitation to a game, he leapt on to the moored punt and chased about exuberantly amongst the scarlet cushions.

Furious at being disturbed, the cat swished her tail in disapproval and smacked out at him with an unsheathed paw.

He dodged the blow expertly and sprang over the seats to the prow, where he braced himself for a moment, then dived into the water with a loud splash.

The little mallards looked at him nervously as he swam across to them, breaking up the placid smoothness of the stream with his flapping paws.

He came closer and, alarmed, the ducklings began to scatter.

In defence of her family, the mother duck hurled herself at him, wings beating the water, beak snapping. A sharp snick on his ear made him yelp and plunge away, barking to show he had as much right to this part of the backwater as she and her family had.

The Siamese cat, mewing with pleasure at the entertainment, came to the edge of the punt to get a grand-stand view.

But the quacks and general clamour drew another curious spectator to the scene. In a burrow in the bank a pair of whiskers twitched menacingly.

. . . . . .

THE rat was large and fat, well into his prime, and breakfast rose uppermost in his thoughts. And for breakfast what could be tastier than duckling ?

He moved silently, a dark grey shape, long, smooth tail swishing as he swam towards his prey . . . the smallest member of the group.

The Odd One sensed nothing of the danger stalking him until two sharply-pointed fangs dug into a soft wing.

With a squeaky quack of terror, the duckling struggled ineffectually in the rat's relentless grip. Feathers flew and tiny webbed feet scrabbled in the

stream as the frantic little creature was hauled back towards the dark entrance to the rat's lair.

Nothing, it seemed, could save The Odd One.

. . . . . .

AND then through the water, streaking along with the speed of light, came a furious, barking form.

The Yorkshire terrier charged full tilt at the rat, sinking his teeth into its neck and forcing open the cruel jaws.

The Odd One escaped, leaving a

trail of torn out feathers, and flapped shakily over to the shelter of his mother's wing.

Fountains of spray filled the air as the two animals, who differed very little in size and strength, battled in a fierce life-or-death struggle for supremacy.

The mother mallard, whose only concern was for her young, gathered them close to the protective shelter of her wings, and with frantic quacks she urged them away downstream.

From a safe vantage point they paused and glanced back.

The fight had reached its climax and suddenly the rat, bruised and battered, with defeat facing him, tore himself free of the Yorkshire terrier and dived into his burrow, disappearing into the narrow caverns.

Exhausted but triumphant, the little dog scrambled on to the landing stage and shook the dripping water from his fur.

One ear was ripped and blood was trickling from a bite above his left eye. But he didn't regret a moment of the day's sport.

He looked about him for the mallard family, but they were already gliding on their way, in line astern.

The Odd One trailed last, as always, a bare patch on his wing where the lost feathers had been.

He was a little older, a little wiser. In one brief morning he had learned who his enemies were. And who his friends were, too.

He hoped they would come this way tomorrow. And that the dog would be there.

BABS OF BUTTERFLY FARM

BARBARA MARLOW'S hobby was butterfly collecting. Recently she had made the catch of a lifetime not far from her home in Suffolk—a butterfly which had flown from America. Little did Babs realise where the news of this capture would lead her!

LOOK—MY DEAR PARENTS, I'M FAMOUS!

YOU AND YOUR PRECIOUS BUTTERFLIES! THEY WON'T BRING YOU MUCH FAN MAIL.

Next day—

GOOD MORNING. DOES HONOURABLE MISSY MARLOW RESIDE HERE, PLEASE?

WELL, I DON'T KNOW ABOUT HONOURABLE, BUT I'M BABS MARLOW.

The Japanese gentleman, who introduced himself as Sessue Kiyawa, asked to see Babs' collection of butterflies.

I READ OF YOUR CAPTURE IN NEWSPAPER AND AM VERY INTERESTED. WOULD LIKE TO SPEAK TO YOUR PARENTS.

I AM BUTTERFLY FARMER, BUT HAVE TOO MUCH WORK FOR SELF ALONE. WOULD BE MOST HONOURED IF YOUR DAUGHTER COMES TO HELP ME. YES?

IT SOUNDS JUST THE JOB FOR BABS!

TO MERESIDE BUTTERFLY FARM
PROP. S.KIYAWA

That very day, Mr Kiyawa drove Babs to his farm.

At Mr Kiyawa's bungalow—

ALLOW ME TO PRESENT MY WIFE, YOKO—THIS IS MISS BABS WHO COMES TO WORK WITH ME.

VERY PLEASED TO MAKE YOUR ACQUAINTANCE.

Two days later—

PLEASE, MY WIFE, YOKO, WILL DRIVE YOU TO THE FILM LOCATION, BABS.

BUT I KNOW NOTHING OF BUTTERFLIES, SO I LEAVE ALL THAT TO YOU.

SESSUE KIYAWA LEPIDOPTERIST

FGB

They arrived on location. Mrs Kiyawa was very nervous.

PLEASE, WE GO BACK. BAD MEN ARE FIGHTING.

It was early afternoon before the director was ready for the butterfly scene.

IT ISN'T A REAL FIGHT, YOKO. IT'S ONLY FOR THE FILM.

WELL—IF YOU ARE VERY SURE. I DO NOT LIKE VIOLENCE.

IN THIS SHOT, OUR HEROINE IS GAZING ACROSS THE RIVER. TO EMPHASISE THE PEACE AND SERENITY, I WANT A BUTTERFLY TO SETTLE ON HER, IF POSSIBLE.

WELL, I'LL TRY. BUTTERFLIES DON'T RESPOND TO DIRECTION, BUT WE HAVE FOUR, IN CASE OF RE-TAKES.

The first butterfly flew off in the wrong direction.

THAT'S A LONG GOODBYE TO HIM!

The second one flew too high for the cameras.

STOP! THIS WON'T DO AT ALL.

YOUR BUTTERFLIES DON'T SEEM TO LIKE ME, DO THEY?

I'VE AN IDEA—DO ANY OF YOU HAVE SWEETS—WITH HONEY IN THEM PREFERABLY?

Janine Grey, the star, kept a packet of honey pastilles with her, to ease her throat during filming. Babs melted them down with some extra sugar.

WHAT'S THE IDEA?

I'M HOPING THIS WILL BE A BAIT FOR OUR BUTTERFLY STAR. WOULD YOU MIND DABBING A LITTLE OF THIS ON YOUR HAIR, MISS GREY?

THE THINGS I DO FOR ART!

Babs held her breath when the third Swallowtail was released.

GO ON...LAND, MY BEAUTY.

SUCCESS! A PERFECT SHOT!

Several weeks later—

HOW FABULOUS—FANCY ME ATTENDING A FILM PREMIERE WITH THE STARS.

Better still was to follow—

SPECIAL SCENIC EFFECTS BY MISS BABS MARLOW

MY NAME ON THE SCREEN! I CAN'T WAIT TO TELL MUM AND DAD, AND THE KIYAWAS.

Later—

THE PREMIERE WAS MARVELLOUS. THE FILM STARS WERE FAB BUT I STILL THINK THE BUTTER-FLIES WERE THE REAL STARS.

The End

Winter Wonderland

Winter is a time when frost and snow produce some gorgeous pictures—and some strange situations to go with them!

Last night we had a fall of snow—
A heavy one, I think.
I went down to the fountain.
But I couldn't get a drink.

I thought I'd come home
                    through the woods
And see the pine trees green,
But there they stood like icicles—
The biggest ever seen.

The lamps were trying very hard
To light the way for me
But frost and ice just wouldn't
Let them do their job, you see.

Next day, poor dad was late for work
Not in a mood for jokes.
The frost had stretched its fingers out
And jammed up all his spokes!

The WONDERLAND of DOLLS

Dolls made of wood, and of wax, china dolls and rag dolls—they all have a story to tell. Perhaps the best-known doll story of all is the old Italian tale by Collodi, called "Pinocchio". This tells of a naughty little wooden puppet called Pinocchio, who is turned into a real, live, human boy by the beautiful Fairy of the Evening Star.

Another well-known story is the folk-tale of "The Little Gingerbread Man," who escaped from the oven and gaily sang:
"Run, run, as fast you can,
You can't catch me—I'm the Gingerbread Man!"

In Yorkshire, baby dolls were often to be seen, made in dough, lightly baked and then dressed in real white baby-clothes!

Another type of doll which has always been popular from earliest times is the Jumping Jack, with his close relative, the Jack-in-the-Box. Dolls that jump about on the end of a string go back to the Ancient Greeks.

A puppet which came to life, with tragic consequences, was the hero of Fokine's famous ballet "Petrouchka." The role was first danced by the most famous male dancer of all time, Vaslav Nijinsky.

Even in the history of Royalty dolls play a part. In the household accounts of King James the First you can read how, when little Princess Elizabeth, his eldest daughter, went on a visit to Scotland, two dolls—written down as "twa babies"—were purchased for her.

Another Royal princess who loved dolls was the late Queen Mary. Born in 1867, she had a fine family of dolls herself when she was a little girl. In Windsor Castle you can see Queen Mary's dolls' house, with tiny portraits on the walls, specially painted by famous artists!

In recent years, soap dolls have become popular around Christmas time as gifts calculated to make even the most reluctant boy or girl eager for a bath. Nursery rhyme characters, and even film stars, have appeared as soap!

Dolls can even make saving up a pleasure! You can still find quaint Victorian money boxes in attics or junk shops. With their jerky mechanical antics, they make it fun to pop a penny in.

Children all over the world love dolls and, realising this, in 1927 the Committee of World Friendship among Children arranged a Doll Festival. Thousands of dolls from all over the United States of America set sail for Japan. There they were put on show in Tokio, and Japanese dolls were sent to America.

Some of these "Friendship Dolls" can still be seen in American museums, reminding visitors that even though the nations of the world may squabble, children can still be friends, wherever they live.

The Wonderland of dolls is indeed a fascinating record of history and geography.

PROBLEM DOG

BOBO was the last born of a litter of six beautiful golden labradors at Kenilworth Kennels. All his brothers and sisters were frisky and full of life—but, somehow, Bobo never joined in the fun.

And Bobo was always held back on a lead while his brothers and sisters were being trained for a very special assignment. Bobo just couldn't understand why he was always "odd dog out".

Then the big day arrived when the other labradors were taken away. The first part of their training was over.

EASY, BOBO! NO USE CRYING— YOU'VE GOT TO STAY HERE AND MAKE THE BEST OF IT.

That night, all alone in his kennel, Bobo howled piteously. No one seemed to care about him, and now he had none of his family to snuggle into at night.

Next morning, Daisy, the kennel maid, had just arrived with Bobo's breakfast—

—when the dog made a sudden lunge for the door, and barged his way past the kennel maid.

Bobo ran and ran as fast as his legs would carry him, and finally crashed through the boundary hedge of the kennels.

Some hours later, Bobo found himself in a muddy country lane. He was trying to seek out his brothers and sisters, but he just couldn't pick up the scent.

Eventually, Bobo arrived on a slip-road close to a busy motorway.

Bobo careered down a steep slope towards the speeding traffic.

And without as much as a sideways glance he raced across the motorway. Cars whizzed by, just missing him by inches.

Later, as Bobo came out of the anaesthetic, he felt the gentle touch of Mavis Blake, the girl who had saved him.

HE'S GOING TO BE ALL RIGHT, MAVIS.

But suddenly, Bobo struggled in his feet and, still very weak, he tottered off.

Mavis followed Bobo to the spacious gardens at the back of the building where blind people and guide dogs were being taught to work together. Bobo's nose twitched excitedly—he had found his brothers and sisters.

The vet arrived to collect Bobo.

WE'VE JUST HEARD THAT THIS IS THE DOG WHO ESCAPED FROM KENILWORTH KENNELS. THEY SUPPLY OUR GUIDE DOGS FOR THE BLIND—BUT THIS DOG IS NO GOOD—POOR THING HE'S BLIND!

But brave Bobo found the love and affection he so much wanted, for Mavis's father agreed to let his daughter keep Bobo.

YOU'VE A BIG JOB ON YOUR HANDS, DEAR! BOBO WILL NEED MORE CARE AND ATTENTION THAN OTHER DOGS, YOU KNOW.

THIS MUSICAL DUMBELL IS JUST THE THING—HE CAN FIND IT BY THE TINKLING SOUND.

DING DONG DING DONG DING

Being blind, Bobo had missed a lot of fun, but his blindness had found him a home and a real friend in young Mavis. The two were going to get along just fine!

THE FIREBUG

MARY COLLINS finished her last mouthful of bacon and, picking up a pencil, added another item to the list at the side of her plate. At the other end of the table her father and brother, Sean, were also going over last-minute arrangements for the next day's horse show.

The morning sunshine poured into the old-fashioned kitchen, lighting up the bright paintwork and the gay dishes on the shelves. The long windows overlooked the stableyard of Collins' Riding School, and on to the wide sweep of the valley and hills beyond. Mary gazed at the view, hoping she'd remembered everything, when smoke rising from a distant farm suddenly attracted her attention.

"Look!" she cried. "There's a fire on the hill! Someone's set fire to the gorse bushes again."

"Oh, no," gasped Mrs Todd, the housekeeper, "not another one!"

"That's the seventh this month," said Sean, "and they still don't know who's doing it. We'll just have to keep our fingers crossed that the firebug doesn't come near us and start setting fire to the buildings here."

At that moment Alec, the groom walked across the yard leading a chestnut mare. Mary forgot the fire and leaned over the window sill.

"Look at Melody," she said admiringly. "She's lovely—but I do wish she'd hurry up and have her foal."

"Oh, it'll be a day or two yet," said her father. "Now let's get on with our preparations. If we don't do well at the show and get a few more pupils it'll be the end of Collins' Riding School."

"Oh, I don't know, Dad. We're not doing too badly," said Sean. "The clients are beginning to trickle in."

"Maybe," said Mr Collins, making for the door. "Anyway, if we do well at the show we may get more business, and I'm hoping to sell Tempest for a good price."

Enter Mr Parker

SEAN and Mary followed him to the stables, but as they reached the yard a car roared up the drive.

"Oh, oh, here comes Parker," muttered Sean.

"Hello, Collins," the newcomer called. "I hear you're not doing so well. Come to help out. Always ready to help a friend."

Mr Collins flushed angrily, and Sean stepped forward, fists clenched.

"Now, now," said Parker soothingly. "Didn't mean to offend."

"We won't give you the chance," said Mr Collins, tight-lipped. "Just leave my property."

Parker studied his nails, smiling.

"I'll buy Tempest," he said after a pause, "and Melody. I hear she's in foal. Foal won't be up to much, but I'll give you £150 the lot."

"Get out! I've experienced your methods of dealing, and I'm not interested!" snapped Mr Collins, and took a step forward. Parker backed to his car.

"O K, I'm going," he snarled, dropping his patronising charm, "but you'll regret it. Particularly when I take over Norloch's school."

He slammed the car door after him and shot down the drive in a cloud of dust.

"What did he mean by that?" asked Mary, startled.

"If he means that Lord Norloch is renting him the covered riding school we might as well give up," replied Sean. "He'll be able to teach in all kinds of weather."

"Oh, it's so beautiful," said Mary. "Those graceful pillars and curved windows, and the gold and white paint. It would be sacrilege if Parker got it."

"That's what I feel, Mary," said Mr Collins.

Was It An Accident?

THE whole family was up early the next morning, preparing for the show. Tempest, a black part-Arab, was led out, his coat gleaming like polished ebony. He whickered excitedly as Sean led him to the horsebox, but as his hoofs echoed loudly on the ramp, the horse reared and swung round, almost jerking Sean off the ground. He calmed the nervous animal, walking him slowly round the yard again.

"I'll take the box down a bit, Sean," called Mr Collins. "Try him off the bank."

Farther down the yard was a grassy slope from which a frightened horse could step straight into the box. Mr Collins climbed into the driving seat and started the engine, while Sean, Mary, and Alec waited to load their various mounts and piles of equipment.

Suddenly Alec pointed and Sean yelled in warning. As the truck backed up the rear wheel slowly left its axle and toppled over, while the truck lurched slightly sideways. Mary grabbed Tempest's rope as Sean ran forward and Mr Collins jumped out.

"How did that happen?" he roared as he bent to examine the wheel. "Someone slackened off all the wheel nuts. This was done deliberately. Did anyone hear anything last night?"

"Jimmy Scott was here, but he didn't stay long," said Alec.

"Oh, yes, Parker's groom," growled Mr Collins. "He could have come back, but we don't know, and we couldn't prove anything definitely. If this had happened on the road it could have been serious. Right, lads, get the wheel on, and not a word to anyone. Just watch Parker's face when Tempest beats his Tobias in the Open Jumping."

Rosettes All Round

MARY sat erect on Rocky. Lady Norloch had just presented her with the coveted red rosette. She stroked Rocky's gleaming neck affectionately, hardly able to keep her face straight, she was so pleased. But, excited as she was, she could hardly keep her eyes off the main ring, where she could just make out the top of Sean's head as he and Tempest went round the course for the jump-off.

"I hope he wins—he must win!" she said to herself, then suddenly-realised that they were waiting for her to lead the prize-winners round the ring. When she finally reached their horsebox, parked in the shade of the trees, Alec was grinning broadly.

"Did Sean win, Alec?" she asked, dropping from the saddle.

"Of course, miss," said the groom. "And it looks as if there's a buyer already."

Mary looked towards the ring in time to see a stranger stop her father and Sean as they led Tempest through the crowd. Some time later her father came over.

"Well, gang, we've excelled ourselves today. Congratulations, Mary. I haven't seen you since your win. I've sold Tempest for a very good price, too, much to Parker's annoyance, so that's two good advertisements for us. Put us in a good mood for the ball tonight, eh? Right, let's pack up —we'll need to hurry to be back in time."

Red (Glow) For Danger

LORD NORLOCH held a ball each year after the annual show for all the competitors, and Mary had a wonderful time with all her Pony Club friends.

Just then a pretty young girl rushed up to Sean.

"Sean," the girl gasped, "I thought I saw a red glow near your place. Is it all right? It couldn't be on fire, could it?"

Sean was halfway down the room before she had finished.

Mr Collins appeared in the doorway of the riding school as they rushed out. He stared unbelievingly at the glow, then dived into his car. The car swung down the drive and turned into the road as a fire engine raced past, heading up the hill. When they reached the yard Mr Collins was out before the car had stopped, running until

a policeman stopped him.

"All right, Mr Collins. The brigade will deal with this. There's nothing you can do."

The stables were gone, the barn a smouldering ruin.

"The horses, Dad!" said Sean, his voice shaking. "I couldn't get near the stables!"

Mary felt the tears running down her face for her favourites— Rocky; Tina, the tiny Shetland; and the beautiful Melody and her unborn foal.

"Was it the fire-raising maniac?" Mr Collins asked.

"No," the policeman replied. "We caught him yesterday on the other side of the county. This was an accident."

"Or someone's pretending to be the firebug," muttered Sean.

The sergeant looked at him.

"Now, who would want to do a thing like that, Sean?"

"You'd be surprised, Sergeant Watkins. You'd be surprised."

Another "Firebug"

MARY turned away, unable to watch the scene any more. Other people had arrived from the dance, Lord Norloch among them. Mary glanced over at the group, then a face in the background attracted her attention. Alec, the groom, was waving to her from the paddock, the reflection from the flames flickering across his face, and on either side, watching interestedly, was a row of pony faces.

"Dad," cried Mary, "look!"

Mr Collins and Sean turned as Mary rushed to the paddock,

hugging Alec, Rocky, Tina, and Alec again, crying with joy.

Alec was grim-faced as the men strode over.

"I got them out, Mr Collins, but I'm sorry I couldn't stop the fire."

"Don't worry, Alec. The main thing is that you're all safe."

"What do you know about this, lad?" asked the police sergeant. "What happened to your face?"

Only then did they notice that Alec's face was bruised and bleeding, one eye fast closing. Alec edged away, almost falling over a bundle propped against the gate.

"I had a wee bit trouble," he admitted. "But I copped him, Mr Collins!"

"Who?"

"The rotter that started the fire."

Mr Collins, his eyes now accustomed to the darkness, saw that the bundle at Alec's feet was a man, expertly trussed and gagged.

"Jimmy Scott, Mr Parker's groom!" exclaimed the sergeant, yanking the hobbled man to his feet. "I always thought I'd have trouble with him one day."

The watcher stood back as a constable led the groom to the car, and Lord Norloch approached Mr Collins.

"I saw Parker clearing out when Scott was arrested. He looked as though he'd had a hand in the fire-raising, but I don't suppose he'll get far," he said. "That solves the problem of how to politely refuse him the covered school. I had no intention of giving it to him. I had you in mind originally, Collins, if you want it."

"Thank you, sir. Not only do I want it, now I really need it," Mr Collins replied.

Just then a high-pitched yell was heard across the yard. Alec jumped.

"Melody! She's in the garage!"

They ran, and when Mary finally picked her way over the debris she found them all busy. In the unaccustomed surroundings of the garage, bedded deep in golden straw, Melody had foaled. By her side was the still damp, long-legged chestnut colt.

"Well, Mary," said her father, "here's our future champion. What do we call this one?"

"There's only one name for him, Dad—The Firebug, of course!"

PET QUIZ

How well do you know your pets? Well enough to answer the following questions, do you think? Test yourself, but remember, NO peeping at the answers first!

1—Which breed of dog does not bark?

2—Can you name the world's smallest breed of dog?

3—Can you name the three breeds of cats shown below?

4—What popular pets are sometimes referred to as cavies?

5—What is the unusual feature about a Manx cat?

6—Is a blind person required to pay a licence on his dog?

7—When is a horse a yearling?

8—To which famous poetess did Flush belong?

17—When was Cruft's dog show founded?

18—Can you pair off the heads with the tails shown below?

19—Can you name the type of animals to be found in the following stories: (a) Dick Whittington; (b) Peter Pan; (c) Heidi?

20—Do you know which countries the following dogs come from: (a) Pekingese; (b) Dachshund; (c) Corgi?

21—What colour are a kitten's eyes at birth?

22—Which dog, according to Greek legend, was supposed to guard the entrance to Hades?

23—Walt Disney made a film about the famous dog, Greyfriars Bobby. In which city would you find a monument to Bobby?

24—Do you know the name of Dick Turpin's famous horse?

9—Can you name the largest breed of horse to be found in Britain?

10—Is the dog on the right: (a) an Alsatian; (b) a Husky; (c) Italian sheep dog?

11—Where does a horse wear: (a) a numnah; (b) a martingale?

12—Which animal was regarded as sacred by the Ancient Egyptians?

13—What is the name given to a young mare?

14—Shown below are three famous people. Can you identify them, and pair each off with the animal or birds associated with them?

15—How many toes in all has a cat?

16—Anna Sewell wrote the autobiography of a horse. What was the horse's name?

25—Can cats swim?

26—To which king do Cavalier Spaniels owe their popularity?

27—Do you know the name of the dogs used by Eskimos to pull their sledges?

28—Do you know where budgerigars can be found in their wild state?

29—The word hand is used in measuring horses. How many inches are there in a hand?

30—What is a garron?

31—What colour are Siamese kittens at birth?

32—Do you know what the Dachshund was used for originally?

ANSWERS

1—The Basenji. 2—The Mexican Chihuahua. 3—(a) Burmese, (b) Blue Persian, (c) Siamese. 4—Guinea pigs. 5—It does not have a tail. 6—No. 7—When it is in its second (calendar) year. 8—Elizabeth Browning. 9—The English Shire horse. 10—Italian sheep dog. 11—(a) Under the saddle, (b) round its neck. 12—The cat. 13—A filly. 14—Pat Smythe (horse), Peter Scott (ducks), Valerie Singleton (dog). 15—18. Four on each hind paw, five on each fore-paw. 16—Black Beauty. 17—1886. 18—A-D, B-E, C-F. 19—(a) Cat, dog. 20—(a) China, (b) Germany, (c) Wales. 21—Blue. 22—Cerberus. 23—Edinburgh. 24—Black Bess. 25—Yes. 26—Charles II. 27—Huskies. 28—Australian. 29—4. 30—A Scottish Highland pony used for hill-trekking. 31—White. 32—Hunting badgers.

FIRST AID
FOR
FOUR-FOOTED FRIENDS

When you buy a pet, you accept all the responsibilities that go with it. You undertake to feed it, groom it and, in some cases, exercise it. Although you don't look for your pet to be ill, animals are just as liable to take ill or have accidents as humans. Naturally, you take your pet to the vet if he is ill, just as you go to the doctor when you are ill. In some cases, however, the injury or illness is such that you can treat it at home. Below are some hints on first aid which you can perform successfully at home.

The photographs shown here show some of the wonderful work carried out by the R.S.P.C.A., whose clinics provide free veterinary treatment for animals, and birds of needy people.

BURNS AND SCALDS

If caused by hot coals, boiling water or fat, apply cold water immediately, dry off gently, and smear the affected area with mineral oil. Consult a vet at once if the burns or scalds are extensive.

CUTS AND SCRATCHES

If the cut or scratch is small, a little antiseptic ointment applied sparingly will clear it up fairly quickly. If the cut is large, however, and bleeds considerably, cut away the surrounding fur - carefully and gently cleanse the wound with moist, warm boracic lint, and cover with a piece of dry boracic lint. Keep the pad in place with a bandage, and remember to change both the lint and the bandage frequently.

SPLINTERS IN THE PAD

First remove any splinter, sharp stones, or glass which may be embedded in the pad, then apply an antiseptic ointment. If the foreign body is too deeply embedded, or if the pad has become septic, take the animal to a vet at once.

POISONING

If an animal has been poisoned, you must always call a vet. While you are waiting for the vet, you can, however, give the animal an emetic, such as salt and water.

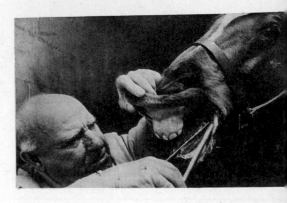

TAR AND PAINT

To remove, apply butter or olive oil freely to the affected area, then wipe off carefully. You may need to repeat this process several times.

MIRANDA'S MYSTERY PLANT

HOWARD! I'VE FOUND A MOST UNUSUAL PLANT! I WONDER WHAT IT'S CALLED. CAN YOU HELP ME?

DON'T BOTHER ME NOW, SIS. CAN'T YOU SEE I'M BUSY?

Miranda Paterson was mad keen on botany — while her brother Howard spent all his spare time inventing things.

I'M SORRY, HOWARD. I KNOW YOU DON'T LIKE TO BE DISTURBED. WHAT'S WORRYING YOU?

The Patersons had a grocery store in a thriving little town in Lincolnshire.

IT'S THE STORE. DAD'S KEEN TO HAVE A BURGLAR ALARM FITTED AND I'M WORKING ON OUR IDEA NOW.

DO-IT YOURSELF BURGLAR ALARM

That day, Miranda set off on another of her tours searching the fields and hedges for unusual plants.

WHY, THERE'S ANOTHER BIG CLUMP OF THAT MYSTERY PLANT!

I KNOW WHO CAN HELP ME.

I'LL ASK OLD HARRY COOPER, THE GARDENER AT THE VICARAGE. HE'S BEEN WORKING WITH PLANTS FOR YEARS 'N YEARS.

At the vicarage.

WHY, I RECKON YOU GOT THERE ONE OF OUR OLDEST INHABITANTS. IT'S WOAD. THE ANCIENT BRITONS USED TO STAIN THEIR BODIES WITH IT.

THAT'S INTERESTING, MR COOPER. HOW IS THE DYE MADE?

WELL, NOW, IF ANYONE SHOULD KNOW ABOUT THAT IT'S GRANNY PERKINS. SHE HAS RECIPES FOR EVERYTHING.

I'D LIKE TO MAKE SOME DYE. THANKS, MR COOPER. I'LL GO AND SEE GRANNY NOW.

Old Granny Perkins was delighted to see Miranda.

COME AWAY IN, MY DEAR. I'LL MAKE A CUP OF TEA AND WE CAN TALK OVER IT.

That day Miranda returned home with an armful of woad.

WHAT'S THAT YOU'VE GOT?

OH, DON'T BOTHER ME NOW, HOWARD. CAN'T YOU SEE I'M BUSY?

Miranda began to carry out the instructions given to her by old Granny Perkins.

GRANNY SAID TO GRIND THE LEAVES INTO A PASTY MASS, WITH LIME WATER.

I CAN SEE THE WATER TURNING BLUE. I'LL HAVE TO WATCH MY HANDS.

While Miranda was busy making dye in the back shop, Howard was trying out his burglar alarm.

Later that week customers began to complain about a funny smell in the shop.

Mr Paterson traced the source of the smell to Miranda's bowlful of woad. The stuff was fermenting nicely.

That night the store was broken into and money taken from the till.

Please turn over two pages for the continuation of this story.

BOTTLE
YOUR
GARDEN

IN Victorian times, large glass domes were used as protective covers on various ornaments around the house.

Nowadays these domes, filled with stuffed birds, clocks or miniature gardens, are valuable collectors' pieces.

You can copy this idea by making miniature gardens for yourself inside glass containers. Who knows, one day your very own miniature garden might be an antique!

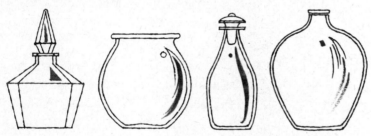

The ideal type of bottle for you to plant your garden in is called a carboy. This kind of container is used in laboratories and factories to hold acid or various types of chemicals.

However, if you can't obtain one of these, any other unusually-shaped bottle or glass container will do. Make sure that the neck is wide enough to get your plants in.

Here is what you will need to plant your garden under glass.

1. A selection of plants.
2. Marble chips or pebbles for drainage.
3. Cardboard tube for filling the container.
4. A long-handled fork such as a toasting fork and a skewer for planting. A long piece of wire and a spray for watering.
5. A bag of sterilised soil—obtainable from a gardening shop.

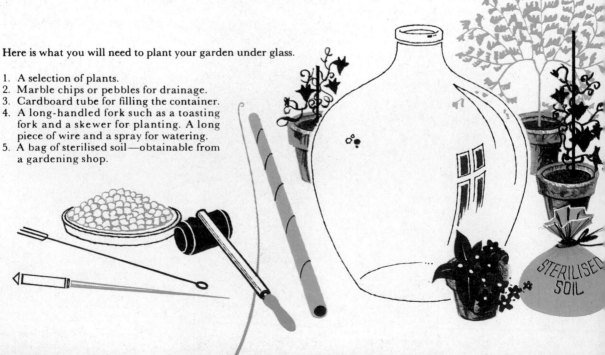

Here is a list of interesting plants you could grow in your bottle garden.

Tradescantia — Wandering Jew. Varieties of *Ivy*. Small *Rock Garden Pinks* (ask permission first before you take it from the garden). Bunches of *Violets, Maidenhair Fern* and *Busy Lizzie*. There are many other pot plants which can be grown successfully in bottles.

A piece of driftwood could be placed in the bottle for effect and also to help support some of the more delicate plants.

An unusual type of bottle garden is one in which you grow herbs. A row of jars containing parsley, thyme or smaller mint plants would look very effective on the kitchen window-sill.

The herbs can be snipped off as you need them to put in your favourite dishes.

To fill the container, first of all make sure it is perfectly clean and dry inside. Roll a tube of paper or use a cardboard tube if you have one, and use it to pour the pebbles or marble chips on to the base of the container. Spread out evenly with a stick. Finally, pour in the soil through the tube, making sure that no particles of soil stick to the side of the bottle.

Pat the soil firmly down and then poke a hollow for the first plant.

With the long piece of wire, make a loop at one end and sit the plant on this, then lower carefully into the hollow in the soil. Cover the roots with plenty of soil and pat firmly in position.

Repeat until all the plants are in position.

You can cover the soil with pebbles or a layer of sand before you spray with water.

Water lightly to begin with, then put the planted bottle in a shady place for a day or two.

If you find you have put too much water into the bottle, leave it open for a time.

As the burglar was helping himself to cigarettes, Howard's burglar alarm went off.

DRAT IT! TIME I WAS OUT OF HERE.

In her bedroom above the store, Miranda heard the alarm bell.

THERE'S SOMEONE IN THE SHOP. I'VE GOT TO WARN DAD AND GET THE POLICE.

When the police arrived, Mr Paterson was counting his losses.

FIFTY POUNDS FROM THE TILL AND FIVE THOUSAND CIGARETTES GONE.

HE BROKE MY BURGLAR ALARM GOING OUT THE BACK WAY, DAD.

HE MAY STILL BE AROUND. TRY THE OUTHOUSES AT THE BACK, OFFICER.

When the outhouses were searched—

LOOK! THE BURGLAR KNOCKED OVER MY BOWL OF BLUE DYE. THAT SHOULD GIVE YOU A CLUE. THE DYE STAINS. IT'S DIFFICULT TO REMOVE.

IF IT'S BEEN IN CONTACT WITH THE SKIN IT COULD BE VERY HELPFUL. WE'LL BE ON THE LOOK-OUT.

Next day the burglar was caught in a transport cafe, sitting drinking tea, with hands that were dyed blue with Miranda's woad.

I'D LIKE YOU TO ACCOMPANY ME TO THE POLICE STATION TO ANSWER SOME QUESTIONS.

Miranda was delighted.

WELL, YOUR BURGLAR ALARM WORKED, HOWARD— BUT IT WAS MY MYSTERY PLANT THAT CAUGHT THE THIEF. I'M OFF TO MAKE MORE DYE.

dear teacher

THE AGONY COLUMN

Our form master is very strict and will not let us change desks. I have fallen out with my friend Ann and wish to sit by Susan, so that Ann can sit by her friend. Would it be best to be friendly with Ann?

Unfriendly, Huddersfield.

Of course, you goose! If you don't, it's going to be a bind to sit by someone to whom you are not speaking, isn't it? And why fall out with anyone, particularly friends. Life's far too short.

At our end-of-term school party there was lipstick on my boy friend's collar. He had the nerve to tell me it was tomato juice. What shall I do?

Stella.

Find out who the tomato was.

Teachers have thirteen weeks' holidays a year, a seven-hour day, with about two hours off for breaks and dinner, and no overtime. We reckon it's a cushy job.

(No names given—I wonder why.)

Well, what about you lot? There are 365 days in the year. If you have only eight hours sleep a night, you spend 122 days in bed. You have about two hours a day for your meals—that makes 30 days a year. You get Sundays and Saturdays off —104 days. And you have 13 weeks, or 91 days' holiday. These add up to 347 days, so you can only spend 18 days at school. And most of that time, I bet, you're asleep.

Your job's *dead* cushy!

What is the longest word in the English language?

Student of Words.

The longest, regularly-formed word is popularly believed to be "antidisestablishmentarianism," which has 28 letters. It was a favourite of W. E. Gladstone, the Victorian statesman, who delighted in using long words and rolling phrases. Look it up to see what it means.

The longest word in the Oxford Dictionary is—wait for it—"floccipaucinihilipilification,"which, as you can see, has 29 letters. It means "the action of estimating as worthless" and is said to have been used by Sir Walter Scott.

In the 18th century a doctor made up a 53-letter word to describe the waters at Bristol Spa, but, not surprisingly, it never got into popular use.

I'm always scared stiff when the 13th of the month comes round, particularly if it falls on a Friday. Is this silly?

Unlucky.

It isn't silly, it's stupid, Unlucky. There's nothing to be afraid of about 13 or a Friday. If you were an Italian girl, you would probably wear a talisman with 13 on it as a protection from evil, because in Italy that number is thought to be one of the luckiest of omens. And if your Dad's pay day is Friday, ask him if he thinks that day is unlucky!

We call our English mistress Dopey because she often falls asleep when she sits down in class. The girls in another of her classes throw a pile of books on the floor when this happens during their lesson. What do you suggest we should do?

"Not A Dopey Fan," Prescot, Lancs.

You could follow your friends' example, but books are meant to be read, not to be thrown about. Why not keep on asking questions so that she has to keep awake? Or what about waiting until she is really off and getting the whole of the class to tiptoe out? That would give her a shock when she awakened and it would be a long time before she dropped off again.

If it really bothers you, you can always have a tactful word with your form mistress and ask her to take it up. Don't be afraid about doing this. Teachers are not paid to fall asleep during lessons and you go to school to be educated, not to watch a sleeping beauty.

Today the whole of our class was kept behind after school for doing nothing. Do you think this is fair?

Form 2A.

It depends on how much nothing you did.

Can you explain why some girls scream when they see a mouse?

Puzzled.

The crusty old bachelor on our staff says that it is often the only proof they can give that they are not cats!

What is a puppy after it's nine days old? *Pat.*

Ten days old.

Why do traffic lights turn red? *Petra.*

Wouldn't you, if you had to change in front of a lot of people and cars?

Although I settle down in the living-room every evening to do my homework, I rarely get it done because I find that I watch the television instead. What do you advise? *Nelly.*

If you examine the telly, Nelly, you will find a knob marked "OFF." If this is turned in the right direction, you'll find it easy to do your homework.

Can you tell me what is the oldest riddle in the world? *Marie.*

Probably the one the Sphinx used to ask —What animal has one voice and is, in turn, four-footed, two-footed and three-footed? Each time the riddle was answered incorrectly, she ate a man. At last King Oedipus gave the proper answer: man, who crawls on all fours when a child, walks on two feet when grown, and walks with the help of a stick in his old age. According to Greek legend, the Sphinx thereupon killed herself.

Who was Christina Willes and what is she famous for?
                                    Maiden Over.

She is the girl who is said to have revolutionised the most masculine of all games—cricket. She lived in the early 19th century and her brother, who was cricket crazy, used to persuade her to bowl to him. At that time, under-arm bowling was the rule and one day Christina found the wide hoop-crinoline she was wearing such a drag that she picked up the ball and bowled over-arm. This soon spread all over the country and is now one of the laws of cricket.

Can girls enter for the Duke of Edinburgh's Award Scheme and, if so, what do we have to do to qualify?

                Three Keen Types.

Yes. It is designed for girls as well as boys and your P.E. mistress or youth club leader should be able to give you all the details.

Briefly, there are three series of tests for girls, starting at the age of 14. There are four sections in each series:—1 Design for Living, 2 Interest, 3 Adventure and 4 Service. You have to reach a certain level in each section before you can go on to the higher series and, starting from scratch, it takes about four years to finish them all. When you pass the first series, you get a letter of commendation and a bronze badge; for passing the second and third there are illuminated certificates signed by the Duke of Edinburgh, with silver and gold badges respectively.

All the awards are worth getting and the work is within the reach of anyone who has average ability and is keen. When you get the gold badge, you may get a trip to Buckingham Palace and a chance of meeting the Duke.

I am a very disappointed girl. I failed my 11 plus and so have to go to the secondary modern instead of the grammar school. Will I still be able to take the G.C.E.?
                        Dunce.

Cheer up, my dear. You are not a dunce because you have not passed the 11 plus. Few people today believe that this exam is a true test of ability or intelligence.

More and more secondary modern schools are entering candidates for the G.C.E. examinations these days and your school will probably be one. If it doesn't enter now, it most probably will in five years' time, when you will be old enough to sit.

Over 30,000 children from secondary modern schools sat this year for the same G.C.E. examinations as children from the grammar. About one out of every ten will get five or more passes and some will do much better than this.

At a secondary modern school I taught at a few years ago, one boy who had failed his 11 plus got eight passes. He is now studying at university and will certainly get a very good degree. There are others like him—girls, too—and there will be many more.

Do all alphabets have 26 letters?
                    Curious.

No. French has 25, Italian 22 and Greek 24. Chinese has no alphabet, but it has more than 2000 characters which must be learned by all who want to read.

ABCDEF GHIJKLM NOPQRS TUVWXYZ

There's a tongue twister craze on at school just now. Can you give me any fresh ones, please?
                Free Fird Formers.

I can see there is. What about, "The old scold sold a school coal scuttle" or "Twixt six thick thumbs stick six thick sticks"?

What did the Irishman tell the chiropodist?
                    Connemara.

My fate is in your hands.

Can you tell me what Preston Tower, in Preston, Suffolk, is famous for?   *Historian.*

It was built in the 17th century by a man called William Latimer as a present for the 13-year-old girl he was courting, Ellen de Preston. It had six storeys with one room on each storey, and each room was marked with the name of the subject Ellen had to study inside it. Tapestry was the subject for the bottom room, then music, painting, arithmetic, literature and astronomy on the top. The surprising thing is that she married him after all that!

My sister is getting married next month and I am to be one of the bridesmaids. Someone has told her that if she thinks of three words connected with the service as she walks up the church, she'll look composed and confident. What three words do you suggest?   *Sally.*

Aisle. Altar. Hymn. Because she no doubt will.

This is rather personal, but please don't giggle. At home I don't have to ask permission to leave the room. Why must I at school?   *Puzzled.*

It puzzles me, too. I suppose the "school answer" is that it's the courteous thing to do, or that if it wasn't the rule everyone in the class would leave the room. Some teachers don't insist on the "hand up, please may I leave the room" procedure and have found that because they trust their pupils their trust is not abused.

What do you think about the latest fashion for mini skirts?
                Fashion Conscious.

Short skirts won't please the Miss
Who's cursed with legs like this () or this)(.

When I last rote to "Deer Teecher," you sed you wear unabel to reed my riting and sujjested that I shud have some practis before I rote to you agen. Wot do you think too this?
                        Molly.

It's much better. Unfortunately, the marked improvement has revealed your complete inability to spell. Spelling practice now, Molly.

I shall be 13 next month and would like to have a birthday party. The snag is that my parents think I'm too old. Do you think so?   *Kate.*

If you want a birthday party, you're not too old, Kate!

We've been doing abbreviations in English. I can get most of them, but some really have me foxed. Why, for example, is cwt. the abbreviation for hundredweight?   *Mystified.*

Because at one time there were 100 pounds in a hundredweight, not 112 as there are today, and C was the Roman symbol for 100. Got it?

Can you answer this? A diesel train was travelling due south and a strong north wind was blowing. Which way did the smoke go?   *Marta.*

You'll have to be smarter, Marta. There's no smoke from a diesel train.

BOUND FOR THE BEACH

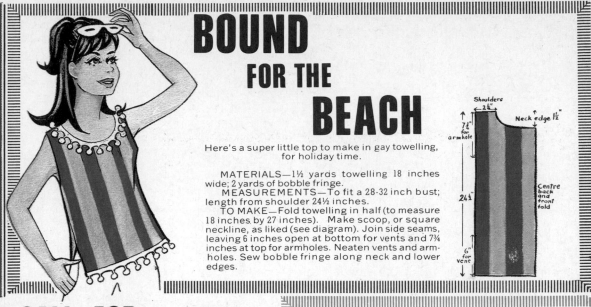

Here's a super little top to make in gay towelling, for holiday time.

MATERIALS—1½ yards towelling 18 inches wide; 2 yards of bobble fringe.

MEASUREMENTS—To fit a 28-32 inch bust; length from shoulder 24½ inches.

TO MAKE—Fold towelling in half (to measure 18 inches by 27 inches). Make scoop, or square neckline, as liked (see diagram). Join side seams, leaving 6 inches open at bottom for vents and 7¾ inches at top for armholes. Neaten vents and armholes. Sew bobble fringe along neck and lower edges.

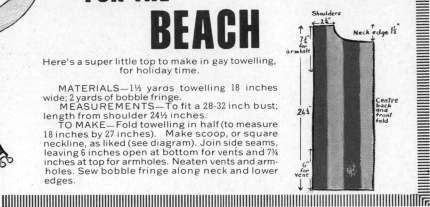

CALL FOR CROCHET

A smart collar and cuff set to make.

MATERIALS — Coats' Chain Mercer-Crochet No. 20 (20 grm.) 1 ball selected colour; a pair of knitting needles No. 13; a crochet hook No. 2½.

SIZE—Collar—approx. 15 inches round neck edge. Cuffs—length, 8 inches.

TENSION—9 sts. and 10 rows to 1 inch over stocking stitch.

ABBREVIATIONS—K. knit; p. purl; st (s) stitches (es); yfd. yarn forward; yrn. yarn round needle; tog. together; sl. slip; psso. pass slipped stitch over; rep. repeat.

THE COLLAR—Cast on 95 sts. K. 2 rows.
3rd ROW—(k.3, yfd.) to last 2 sts., yfd., k.2.
4th ROW—p.1, (p.2, yrn., p.2 tog.) to last st., p.1.
5th ROW—k.1, (k.2, yfd., sl. 1, k.1, psso.) to last st., k.1. Rep. last 2 rows 10 times, then rep. 4th row again.

NEXT ROW—k.2 (work k.1, p.1 into yrn., k.3) to end. K. 2 rows. Cast off loosely.

THE CUFFS—Cast on 62 sts. K.2 rows.
3rd ROW—k.1, (k.2, yfd., sl. 1, psso.) to last st., k.1.

4th ROW—p.1, (p.2, yrn., p.2 tog.) to last st., p.1. Rep. last 2 rows 11 times more. K.3 rows. Cast off loosely.

TO MAKE UP—Work a row of double crochet along side edges of cuffs and collar if required to make a firm edge. Stretch work lightly, pin out flat and leave to dry.

KNIT NATTY HATS

MATERIALS—3 oz. of Jaeger Tropic-Spun; a pair of No. 6 knitting needles.

SIZE—To suit head sizes up to 22 inches.

ABBREVIATIONS—K.—knit; p.—purl; st(s).—stitch(es); tog.—together; beg.—beginning; dec.—decrease.

TO MAKE—Cast on 72 sts. and work 3 inches in k.1, p.1 rib. Now continue in k.3, p.3 rib until work measures 9½ inches from beg.

Dec. Row—(K.3, p.3 tog.) to end.
Next Row—(K.1, p.3) to end.
Dec. Row—(K.3 tog., p.1) to end.
Work 1 row in k.1, p.1 rib.

Break off yarn, run end through remaining sts., draw up and fasten off.

TO MAKE UP—Join back seam. Fold up lower edge. Brush right side of hat lightly. Make a tassel by winding yarn over a 3-inch piece of cardboard 70 times. Cut strands at one side, then, using yarn double, tie strands securely at centre. Sew tassel to top of hat.

MATERIALS.—3 oz. of Patons Double Quick Knit; a pair of No. 3 knitting needles.

SIZE.—To fit head sizes up to 22 inches.

ABBREVIATIONS.—K.—knit; p.—purl; st(s).—stitch(es); beg.—beginning; tog.—together; sl.—slip.

TENSION.—10 sts. (2 patterns) to 2½ inches.

NOTE.—Use 2 strands of wool tog. throughout.

TO MAKE.—Cast on 32 sts. and k.1 row. Continue in patt. thus:
1st row (wrong side).—K.2, (p.3, winding wool twice round needle for every st., k.2) to end.
2nd row.—P.2 (sl. next 3 sts., dropping extra loops, then place these 3 sts. back on left-hand needle; now work k.1, p.1, k.1 into the group of 3 sts., p.2) to end.
These 2 rows form patt. Rep. them 31 times more. Cast off.

THE CROWN.—Pick up and k. 40 sts. along right-side edge.
1st and every following alternate row.—P.
2nd row.—(K.3, k.2 tog.) to end.
4th row.—(K.2, k.2 tog.) to end.
6th row.—(K.1, k.2 tog.) to end.
8th row.—(K.2 tog.) to end.

Break wool, run end through remaining sts., draw up and fasten off.

TO MAKE UP.—Join back seam including crown. Fold under 2 p. sts. along lower edge of hat and hem. Press seams and hem lightly.

STRING THINGS

THESE dainty little figures and baskets are easy and cheap to make if you have nimble fingers and plenty of string.

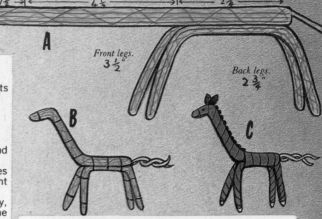

THE GIRAFFE

1½" 4½" 2¼"

A

Front legs. 3½"

Back legs. 2¾"

B

C

To make the giraffe you will need:—

Flax string. (The kind used for bundling newspaper packets together. Used in newspaper agencies and post offices.)

Three yards of beige bias binding.

Two tiny pieces of brown felt or leather for ears.

Brown wool for embroidering the mane.

Brown paint for painting body pattern.

Generally, you will need the same amount of string for the neck and body part as for all four legs.

Begin by cutting eight strands of string (seven to be eight inches long and the other ten inches long) for the neck and body. Also eight strands (each eight and a half inches long) for the legs.

When you come to fasten the pieces together for the neck and body, the extra-long strand will stick out by two inches to form the tail. The string for the legs should be divided into two sets of four strands. Fasten all string parts loosely together before winding. And see diagram B for method of binding the legs to the body.

Next, wind on the bias binding, starting from the nose to base of the neck, and continuing down the front legs. Leave the ends of the legs uncovered to indicate the hoofs. Wind the binding round the rest of the body and the back legs.

Cut and stitch the end of the binding in place.

To make the mane, embroider in blanket stitch and then stitch the ears in place.

Paint eyes on the head and markings on the body.

THE HORSE

To make the horse, work in the same way as for the giraffe, but use string eight and ten inches long for the body (two of the strands being extra long to provide a tail) and nine and a half inches long for the legs. To bind the body use three yards of brown bias binding.

The completed horse, the ballerina and the cowboy.

THE BALLERINA

You will need:—

Flax string.
Two yards flesh-coloured bias binding.
Small piece of net for the skirt.
Narrow white ribbon.
A cocktail stick.

An oak apple.
Pink lacquer paint.
Black embroidery silk.
Needle and pink thread.

The oak apple, for the head, should be dipped in a solution of size (one teaspoonful to a cup of warm water) and allowed to dry. Then paint with pink lacquer.

THE COWBOY   THE BALLERINA

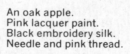

TOP OF HAT
Cut two pieces.

HAT   Cut two pieces

Cut one piece.

Stitch to centre of hat.

TROUSERS
Cut two pieces.

Cut division for legs.

JACKET   Cut two pieces.

Stitch shoulders.

Slit centre front.

The cowboy is made in the same way as the ballerina, using three strands of string for the body and legs.

Using the pattern shown, cut out the costume and stitch where indicated. Decorate with gold cord.

To make the ballerina. Cut two strands of string each five and a half inches long for the arms and two strands each ten inches long for the body and legs.

Fold the body strands over the centre of the arms. Secure with thread and, leaving five inches of the body, divide the string into two legs.

Place the head on the cocktail stick and pierce through the neck.

Wind the body with bias binding and trim hands and feet to a point.

To make the hair, glue on embroidery thread. Paint on features.

To dress the ballerina, stitch the white ribbon criss-cross round the body. Gather the net to make the skirt and stitch in place round the doll.

STRING MATS AND BASKETS

You will need:—

Flax string and ordinary garden raffia.

A needle with an eye big enough to thread the raffia through.

To make a mat, start by winding the string in a coil from the centre. Two strands of string are held in place by the raffia binding (diagram B). When the spaces between X and X have become too large, increase raffia stitching as shown.

Keep coiling the string until you reach the size of mat you require. To finish off the ends, secure on the wrong side and cut off. (See diagram A.)

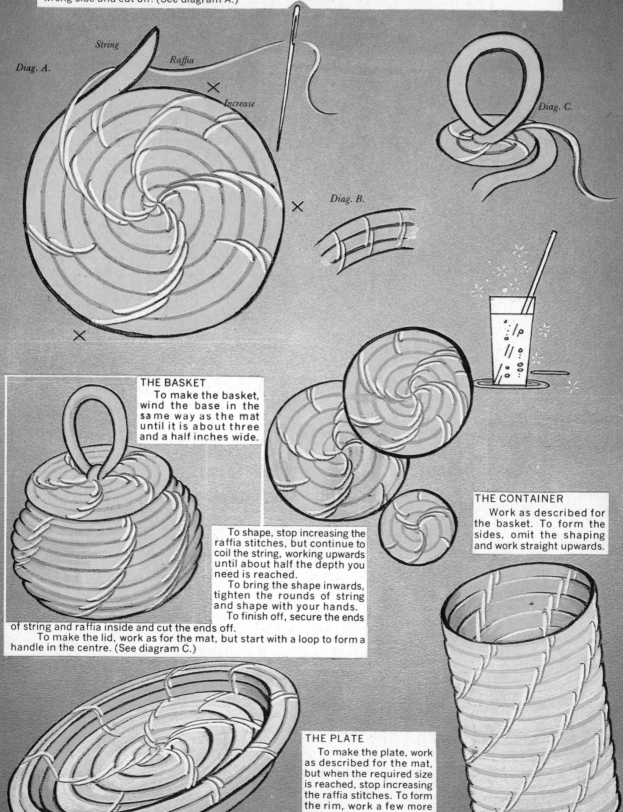

Diag. A.

String

Raffia

Increase

Diag. B.

Diag. C.

THE BASKET

To make the basket, wind the base in the same way as the mat until it is about three and a half inches wide.

To shape, stop increasing the raffia stitches, but continue to coil the string, working upwards until about half the depth you need is reached.

To bring the shape inwards, tighten the rounds of string and shape with your hands.

To finish off, secure the ends of string and raffia inside and cut the ends off.

To make the lid, work as for the mat, but start with a loop to form a handle in the centre. (See diagram C.)

THE CONTAINER

Work as described for the basket. To form the sides, omit the shaping and work straight upwards.

THE PLATE

To make the plate, work as described for the mat, but when the required size is reached, stop increasing the raffia stitches. To form the rim, work a few more coils.

Secure the ends and break off.

Knit a sweater and beret set that's—

ON TARGET!

THE SWEATER

MATERIALS: 13(14) (15) balls of Lister Bel Air Courtelle Double Crepe Knitting in white and 2 balls in navy; a pair each Nos. 9 and 10 knitting needles.

MEASUREMENTS: To fit a 27/28(29/30)(31/32) inch bust; length from shoulder, 20¾(21½)(21¾) inches; sleeve seam, 14½ (15½)(16½) inches. Beret, 9 inches in diameter.

TENSION: 6 sts. to 1 inch over stocking stitch on No. 9 needles.

ABBREVIATIONS: K.—knit; p.—purl; st.(s.)— stitch(es); st.st.—stocking stitch; tog.—together; beg., —beginning; tbl.—through back of loop; rep.—repeat; patt. — pattern; inc. — increase; dec.—decrease; W.—white; N.—navy.

NOTE: Instructions for the larger sizes are in brackets; where only one figure is given, this applies to all sizes.

SWEATER.
The Back. With No. 10 needles and W. cast on 92 (98)(104) sts. Beg. with k., work 7 rows in st.st.

Next Row: k. to mark hemline.

Change to No. 9 needles and continue in st.st. Work 16 rows. Join N. and with N. work 12 rows in st.st. Break N. and continue with W. only. Work straight until back measures 14(14½)(14½) inches from hemline.

Shape Armholes. Cast off 5 sts. at beg. of next 2 rows, then dec. 1 st. at both ends of every row until 70(76)(82) sts. remain. * Continue straight until back measures 20¾(21½)(21¾) inches from hemline, ending with a p. row.

Shape Shoulders. Cast off 7(8)(9) sts. at beg. of next 4 rows and 7 sts. at beg. of following 2 rows. Slip remaining 28(30)(32) sts. on a st. holder.

The Front. Work as for back to *. Continue straight until front measures 19¼ (20)(20¼) inches, ending with a p. row.

Shape Neck. Next row: k. 27(29)(31), turn and continue on these sts., leave remaining sts. on a spare needle. ** Dec. 1 st. at beg. of next and following 5 alternate rows: 21(23)(25) sts.

Shape Shoulder —Cast off 7(8)(9) sts. at beg. of next and following alternate rows. Work 1 row.
Cast off remaining 7 sts. Slip the centre 16(18)(20) sts. on a st. holder. Rejoin wool to neck edge of remaining sts. K. 1 row and p. 1 row. Now work as for first side from ** to end.

The Sleeves. With No. 10 needles and W. cast on 38 (42)(44) sts. Beg. with k., work 7 rows in st.st.

Next Row: K. to mark hemline.

Change to No. 9 needles and continue in st.st. Work 16 rows, increasing 1 st. at both ends of 9th and the following 6th row. Join N. and work in stripe patt. thus, increasing 1 st. at both ends of every 6th row; 8 rows N., 10 rows W., 8 rows N. Break N. and continue with W. only, still increasing at both ends of every 6th row until there are 68(72)(76) sts. Continue straight until sleeve measures 14½(15½) (16½) inches from hemline.

Shape Top. Cast off 5 sts. at beg. of next 2 rows. Dec. 1 st. at beg. of every row until 52(52)(54) sts. remain, then at both ends of every row until 20(20)(22) sts. remain. Cast off.

The Neck Border. Join right shoulder seam. With No. 10 needles and W. pick up and k. 18 sts. down left side of neck, k. the 16(18)(20) centre sts., pick up and k. 18 sts. up right side of neck and k. the 28(30)(32) sts. from back neck: 80(84)(88) sts. Work 7 rows in k.1 tbl., p.1 rib. Cast off loosely.

To Make Up. — Press lightly.

Sweater—Join left shoulder and neck border seam. Join side and sleeve seams. Set in sleeves. Fold under hems at lower edge and sleeves and slip-st. in position. Press seams and hems lightly.

THE BERET

With No. 10 needles and W., cast on 96 sts. Work 8 rows in k.1, p.1 rib. Continue in st.st. thus:
1st row: (k.7, inc. in next st.) to end.
2nd and every following alternate row: p.
3rd row: (k.8, inc. in next st.) to end.
5th row: (k.9, inc. in next st.) to end.
7th row: (k.10, inc. in next st.) to end.
Continue to inc. thus until there are 180 sts. Work 5 rows straight. Join N. and with N. work 8 rows straight. Break N. and continue with W. Work 2 rows straight.
Next row: (k.13, k.2 tog.) to end.
Next and every following alternate row: p.
Next row: (k.12, k.2 tog.) to end.
Continue to dec. in this way until 48 sts. remain, ending with a p. row. Break W. and continue with N.
Next row: (k.2, k.2 tog.) to end. P. 1 row.
Next row: (k.1, k.2 tog.) to end. P. 1 row.
Next row: (k.2 tog.) to end.
Break wool, run end through remaining sts., draw up and fasten off. Join row ends to form centre back seam.
Cut a circle of cardboard 9 inches in diameter. Insert this into beret (wrong side of work facing). Press lightly. Remove cardboard.

KITTY'S CONCERT PARTY

Kitty Coles and her pals have formed a concert party which tours around the countryside, performing for fun in all sorts of places.

Kitty got home from rehearsal one night to find a letter waiting for her.

ON BEHALF OF THE INHABITANTS OF MIDGEWORTH, I AM WRITING TO ASK IF YOU AND YOUR CONCERT PARTY WILL PUT ON A PERFORMANCE IN OUR VILLAGE HALL ON THE 8TH...THE 8TH? THAT'S THIS SATURDAY. BUT WHERE ON EARTH IS MIDGEWORTH?

MIDGEWORTH...MIDGEWORTH? THAT'S ABOUT SEVEN MILES T'OTHER SIDE O' GLORESBURY. AIN'T MET ANYBODY FROM THERE IN YEARS.

THANKS, GRANDPA. IT MUST BE A QUAINT LITTLE PLACE. IT'S QUITE NEAR, YET I NEVER HEARD OF IT. WE'LL THINK OF A PROGRAMME THAT WILL LIVEN THEM ALL UP!

On Friday evening, the gang declared they were quite keen to go to Midgeworth—all, that is, except Valerie Thorne, who was never keen on anything!

I THINK IT SOUNDS PERFECTLY AWFUL! I'M SURE THEY WON'T APPRECIATE MY DANCING THERE.

DON'T WORRY, VAL. I'VE THOUGHT UP A TUNE TO GET THEM GOING, AND INTRODUCE OURSELVES WITH. MAYBE KITTY CAN PUT WORDS TO IT.

The gang listened as Peter Potter, the group's pianist, tinkled out his new tune.

MM—THAT'S TERRIFIC, PETER. HOW ABOUT—HERE WE ARE TO BRING YOU SUNSHINE, LAUGHTER DRIVES AWAY THE RAIN, HERE WE ARE TO MAKE YOUR SKY BLUE...

...THEN WE'LL ALL GO HOME AGAIN!

HO, HO! YOU'D BETTER STICK TO DANCING, VAL. POETRY ISN'T YOUR STRONG SUIT. LEAVE THE LYRICS TO KITTY.

I THINK YOU'RE ALL PERFECTLY HORRIBLE! I'M GOING TO PRACTISE MY DANCES NOW. PLEASE DON'T DISTURB ME.

OH, GOLLY, I SAID THE WRONG THING. SHE'S OFF TO SULK AGAIN.

Later, Kitty went down to the railway station to inquire about a train to Midgeworth.

THE LAST TRAIN TO MIDGEWORTH RAN OUT OF THIS STATION ABOUT THIRTY-FIVE YEARS BACK, MISS. YOU MIGHT GET A BUS AT GLORESBURY.

So, on Saturday, the concert party set off in good time and soon arrived in the market place at Gloresbury, from where the local buses left.

MIDGEWORTH? NO BUSES FOR THERE, MISS. SORRY.

HALLO, THERE! ARE YOU THE PEOPLE WHO ARE GOING TO ENTERTAIN AT MIDGEWORTH? I'M MISS JOLLY, AND I'M HERE TO TAKE YOU DOWN TO THE VILLAGE.

OH, GOOD, WE WEREN'T LOOKING FORWARD TO A SEVEN-MILE HIKE.

WHERE IS YOUR CAR?

CAR? DON'T HAVE ONE. WOULDN'T BE A BIT OF USE ON THE FARM. HOPE YOU DON'T MIND TRAVELLING IN THIS.

A CATTLE TRUCK? THE VERY IDEA!

CHEER UP, VAL, IT'LL BE FUN!

The gang had no choice. It was the cattle truck—or sore feet! So in they piled. As they went along they practised their song.

WE ARE HERE TO BRING YOU SUNSHINE...

But when they first saw the village, they didn't feel so much like singing!

OH, CHARMING, AND I DON'T THINK. WHAT ON EARTH PERSUADED YOU TO COME HERE?

THE HALL IS JUST ROUND THE CORNER. THERE'S ONLY ONE STREET, SO YOU CAN'T MISS IT.

Worse and worse! The "hall" was an ancient Army hut.

AH, YOU MUST BE THE CONCERT PARTY. I'M MISS SIMMS, WHO WROTE FOR YOU TO COME.

SHE WON'T BE MUCH HELP IF WE NEED ANYTHING LAID ON AT THE LAST MINUTE.

Inside the crumbling hut, Peter Potter tried out the ricketty old piano.

IT'S A BIT OUT OF TUNE. I'LL TRY A FEW LOUD CHORDS...

LOOK OUT, PETER! THE CEILING'S CAVING IN!

Peter jumped to safety—just before the ceiling collapsed, covering the piano in rubble!

OH DEAR! OH, DEAR, DEAR!

THAT DOES IT! WE NEED A NEW PIANO AND A NEW HALL. WE'VE GOT 45 MINUTES! GET LOOKING!

The vicar was willing to lend his piano, but the gang couldn't get it out through the door!

I DON'T UNDERSTAND! IT MUST HAVE COME IN AT SOME TIME.

IT'S SO OLD I RECKON THE HOUSE WAS BUILT ROUND ABOUT IT.

Kitty sought out Miss Jolly,

YOU NEED A HALL? I THOUGHT THAT OLD HUT WOULD CAVE IN ONE DAY. WELL I HAVE A SORT OF STUDIO WHERE I PRACTISE THE PIANO. WAIT TILL I'VE FINISHED WITH THIS POOR, SICK LITTLE CHAP.

Miss Jolly's "little studio" was simply a couple of old cottages with the adjoining wall knocked down. On a little platform was a superb grand piano!

WOULD THIS DO? I COULD LAY ON SOME FORMS.

THIS IS MARVELLOUS. IF WE WANT TO GET FROM ONE SIDE OF THE STAGE TO THE OTHER WE CAN CLIMB OUT OF THE WINDOWS AND NIP ROUND THE BACK! AND WHAT A GORGEOUS PIANO! I'LL FETCH THE REST OF THE GANG.

When the rest of the concert party arrived, they all wanted a last-minute practice.

I MUST POLISH MY PLIES...OOPS!

WATCH OUT, THE PIANO LID...

Bang! The heavy lid of the grand piano slammed down on poor Peter's fingers.

OH, VALERIE, LOOK WHAT YOU'VE DONE! POOR PETER WON'T BE ABLE TO PLAY NOW.

I COULD PLAY FOR A LITTLE WHILE, TO LET YOU PRACTISE.

Miss Jolly sat down at the grand—and how she played!

THAT'S GREAT! COULD YOU PLAY FOR US AT THE SHOW?

OH, I COULDN'T POSSIBLY—I'VE A SICK PIGLET TO LOOK AFTER, AND THERE'S NOBODY TO HELP ME ON THE FARM.

VALERIE, THIS CRISIS IS YOUR FAULT. AND THE SHOW STARTS IN TEN MINUTES.

WELL, REALLY, YOU DON'T EXPECT ME TO NURSE A PIG, DO YOU? I'M HERE TO DANCE.

IF YOU DID GO, I COULD STAY AND PLAY. JUST KEEP HIM WARM.

WELL, VALERIE—ARE YOU A MEMBER OF THE TEAM OR DO YOU JUST CARE ABOUT YOUR OWN ACT?

Turning without a word, Valerie climbed out of the window.

WHAT...WHERE ARE YOU GOING, VALERIE?

SHE'S AWAY TO SULK SOMEWHERE AGAIN.

But Valerie wasn't sulking. She took the quickest way to Miss Jolly's farm and back—with the sick piglet. And it was an ordeal!

KEEP AWAY FROM ME! PLEASE KEEP AWAY!

Minutes later, Kitty and her folk group were finishing a song, and Kitty was very worried, for Valerie was due to dance, and Miss Jolly wanted away to see to her pig. Then Valerie arrived—

JUST IN TIME... I HOPE.

With the piglet being looked after, it was—on with the show!

YOU KNOW—WE OWE VALERIE AN APOLOGY. SHE'S A TROUPER!

The performance was going down well. At the interval—

WE'RE ALL TERRIBLY GRATEFUL TO YOU FOR PLAYING. YOU'RE A MARVELLOUS PIANIST.

I USED TO BE A PROFESSIONAL BUT THAT'S ALL PAST. I'M A COUNTRY GIRL NOW. MY PIGS NEED ME.

At the end of the show, Kitty's Concert Party repeated their new signature tune.

HERE WE ARE TO BRING YOU SUNSHINE... LAUGHTER DRIVES AWAY THE RAIN. HERE WE ARE TO MAKE YOUR SKY BLUE...

...THEN WE'LL ALL GO HOME AGAIN!

IN THIS SPECIAL DIANA QUIZ, LOOK AT THE PICTURES OF THESE WELL-KNOWN MUSICIANS AND TRY TO PAIR THEM OFF WITH THE MUSICAL INSTRUMENTS WHICH MADE EACH FAMOUS.

YEHUDI MENUHIN

MYRA HESS

JULIAN BREAM

LEON GOOSSENS

CHRIS BARBER

LOUIS ARMSTRONG

DOUBLES

SHIRLEY ABICAIR

JIMMY SHAND

HARPO MARX

PABLO CASALS

LARRY ADLER

ACKER BILK

ANSWERS.

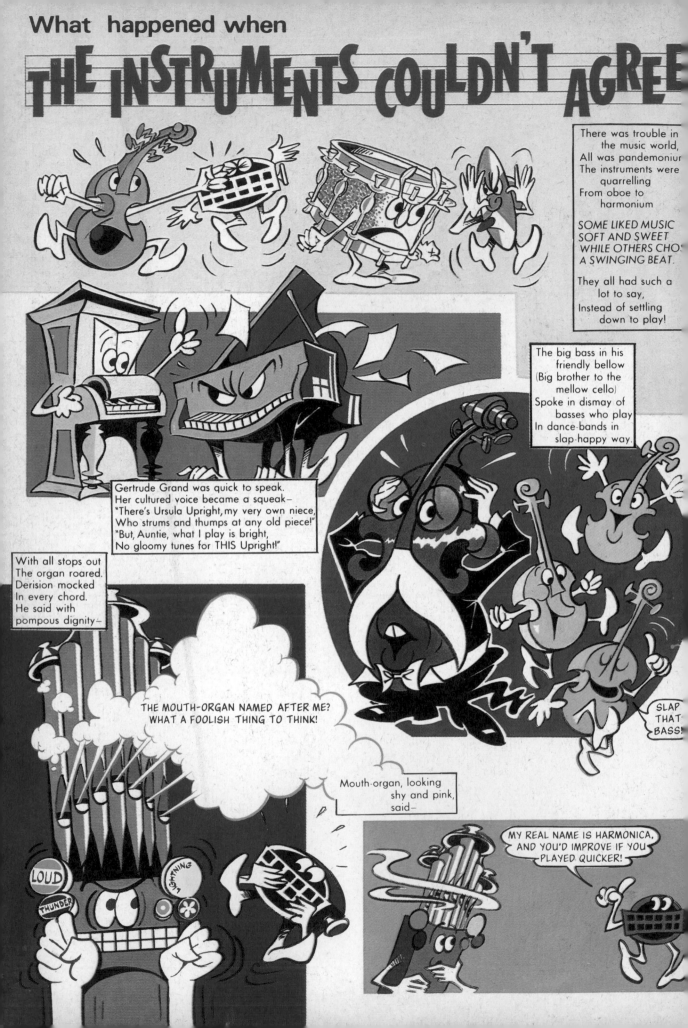

The cymbals clashed down on the flute
Who said he didn't care a hoot!

The violins were very sharp
And quite upset the little harp.

This went on both night and day
Until the drum boomed out to say—

MUST YOU MAKE THAT DREADFUL NOISE? STOP AND THINK—AND REALISE THAT MUSIC, WHETHER GRAND OR GAY WILL ONLY COME BY PLAYING ONE WAY. NO MORE SHOUT AND NO MORE SCREAM PLAY TOGETHER AS A TEAM! I'LL SET THE RHYTHM, BETTER FAR THAN BEATLE-BEAT BY RINGO STARR!

And soon sweet music filled the air,
All around and everywhere.

Tchaikovsky THE MUSIC MAKER

Little Peter Tchaikovsky, who lived in Votinsk, near St Petersburg in Russia, loved to listen to the Mozart music on his father's orchestrion—a kind of musical box. At the age of five, he composed his first song and taught it to his cousin and elder brother.

At school, Peter was only interested in his piano lessons. His father sent him to Law School and he became a government clerk. But often he was in trouble with his boss for working out and writing down the tunes that kept running through his brain.

Peter gave up his job and became a pupil at the St Peterburg Conservatory of Music, where his professor was the great Anton Rubenstein. When Rubenstein gave him a theme on which to compose ten variations, Peter astounded him by turning up next morning with no less than 200!

Peter was happy working with music and wrote some serious compositions which were well received. One morning he heard a plasterer singing at his work. Peter invited him in and wrote down his song.

So well did Peter do at St Petersburg that when Rubenstein's brother started a Conservatory in Moscow, Peter Tchaikovsky's teacher recommended him as Professor of Theory and Composition. So, suddenly, Peter found himself a teacher instead of a pupil!

Later he used it as the theme for an "Andante Cantabile"—the slow movement of a famous string quartet. The great writer, Leo Tolstoi, was moved to tears by Peter's arrangement of the plasterer's song.

Peter was interested in the folk-music of many lands. Once, on holiday in Italy, he heard a little boy singing a catchy little song which became the inspiration for his own song, "Pimpinella." While in Italy, Peter lived near a cavalry barracks. The bugle call he heard every morning introduces his popular "Capriccio Italien."

Peter Tchaikovsky had always been subject to moods of deep depression. He put all his sadness into his Sixth Symphony, the "Pathetique", which he felt was the best music he had ever written. At the age of 53, during a plague of cholera, he died, leaving a wealth of beautiful music for orchestra, opera and ballet.

THE MERRY MERMAIDS

THE girls of the Stanbridge Synchronised Swimming Team — known locally as the Mermaids — are in great demand. Under their expert trainer, Mrs Dot Cameron, they travel all over the country putting on their special displays.

One evening after a training session, Dot had a super surprise for the team.

SMASHING! VICTOR CARLSEN'S THE FAMOUS MILLIONAIRE! WHOOPEE!

WE'VE BEEN INVITED TO PUT ON A DISPLAY AT THE TWENTY-FIRST BIRTHDAY PARTY OF VICTOR CARLSEN'S DAUGHTER, LUCILLA.

In her excitement, Sheila, one of the Mermaids, accidentally knocked another girl into the pool.

TAKE IT EASY, SHEILA. ALTHOUGH WE'RE TO BE GUESTS OF A MILLIONAIRE—IT WILL MEAN HARD WORK AND LOTS OF PRACTICE.

The Mermaids practised harder than ever before, especially on the night that Mr Carlsen's secretary, Bill Harris, arrived.

THEIR ROUTINE FITS INTO MR CARLSEN'S PROGRAMME SCHEDULE NICELY. CALL THEM OVER NOW, I'D LIKE TO HAVE A WORD WITH THEM.

THE GUESTS WILL BE ARRIVING AT MR CARLSEN'S RIVER MANOR BY BOAT. THE WHOLE PARTY IS PLANNED TO BE LIKE AN ANCIENT ROMAN FESTIVAL. EVERYONE WILL BE IN FANCY DRESS EXCEPT YOU GIRLS, BUT MR CARLSEN WANTS YOU TO JOIN IN THE FUN AFTER YOUR ACT.

Before a very interested audience, Dot revealed the secret of the bunches grapes. She explained how her suspicions had been aroused when Sandra had sat on the grapes and they hadn't squashed to pulp, as real grapes would have done.

The Carlsens were overjoyed when the necklace was restrung and returned to the jewel-box safe and sound again.

HERE ARE THE PEARLS. EACH ONE HIDDEN INDIVIDUALLY IN THESE BUNCHES OF IMITATION GRAPES.

THESE PEOPLE WERE IMPOSTERS WHO TRICKED THEIR WAY INTO MY PARTY.

I'LL SEE THAT YOU GET A REWARD FOR THIS—NOW BACK TO THE POOL TO FINISH YOUR WONDERFUL DISPLAY.

The interruption hadn't upset the girls one little bit—in fact, they swam better than ever.

AND NOW, A LITTLE TOKEN OF OUR THANKS. JONES, BRING IN THE BOXES.

At the end of the display, the girls were cheered to the echo.

Dot Cameron and each girl in the team received a superb silver brooch.

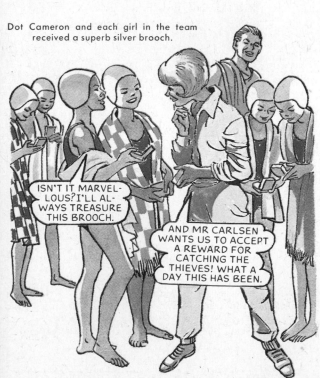

ISN'T IT MARVELLOUS? I'LL ALWAYS TREASURE THIS BROOCH.

AND MR CARLSEN WANTS US TO ACCEPT A REWARD FOR CATCHING THE THIEVES! WHAT A DAY THIS HAS BEEN.

HOORAY FOR THE MERMAIDS.

WE'LL USE THE MONEY TO HELP OTHER GIRLS LESS FORTUNATE THAN OURSELVES ENJOY SWIMMING AND WATER BALLET.

HEAR! HEAR!

THE JOYS

OF SPRING

WHAT IS A TRAMPOLINE? The word "trampoline" means a kind of springboard—it comes from the Spanish and German. A trampoline should consist of a taut nylon sheet stretched between a steel frame and supported by elastic or steel springs.

WHAT IS TRAMPOLINING? A tip-top way of having fun and exercise by bouncing up, down, backwards, forwards, round and round. Trampolining has now become a highly-skilled, competitive, sporting event in its own right.

DO'S AND DON'TS ON THE TRAMPOLINE

Never use the trampoline on your own—at least four supervisors or "spotters," as they are called, should always be standing by ready to assist you if you move too close to the frame edge.

Never play the fool on a trampoline.

Keep the height of your jumping down until you gain experience—15 inches is enough to start with.

Wear light-weight clothes and footwear and remove all sharp objects from pockets.

Make sure you have at least 16 feet of headroom from the floor to the nearest overhanging obstacle.

Know where the first-aid box is.

Always get permission from your instructor before attempting any new exercises.

School on Ice

IRIS LLOYD-WEBB is professional ice skating teacher at Queen's Ice Club, London. She teaches for nine hours a day, six days a week.

A GOLD medallist in ice dancing at the age of 16, Iris loves coaching ice dancing.

MOST pupils are ambitious young girls. Here Jane is being put through her paces by her teacher, who must be patient and understanding. Who knows? Jane, too, may become a skating teacher in years to come.

RODEO-OH-OH!

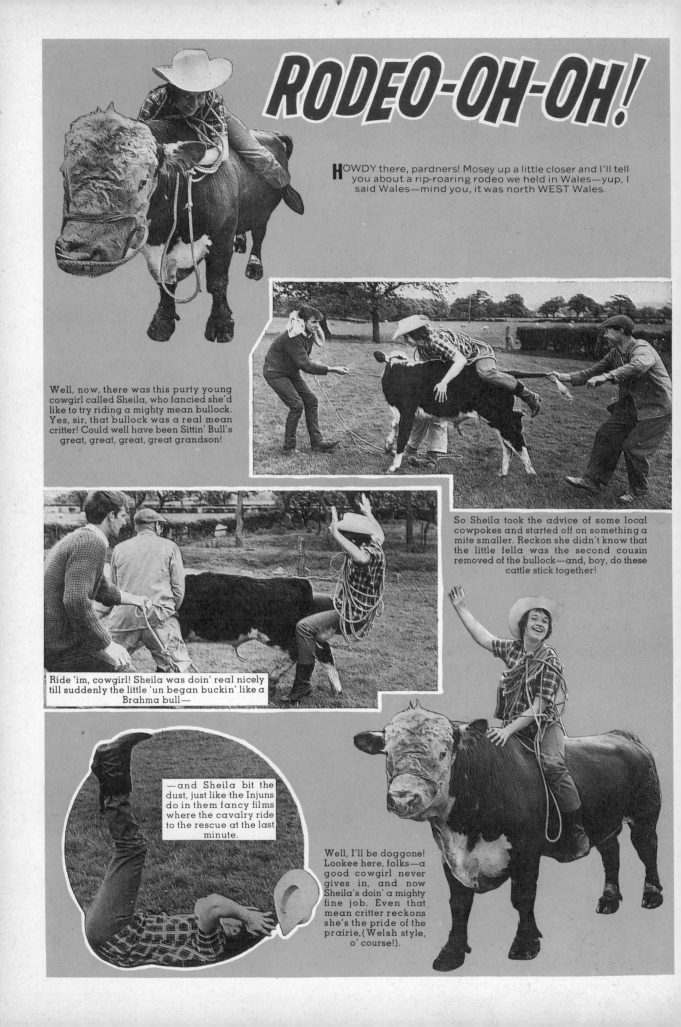

HOWDY there, pardners! Mosey up a little closer and I'll tell you about a rip-roaring rodeo we held in Wales—yup, I said Wales—mind you, it was north WEST Wales.

Well, now, there was this purty young cowgirl called Sheila, who fancied she'd like to try riding a mighty mean bullock. Yes, sir, that bullock was a real mean critter! Could well have been Sittin' Bull's great, great, great, great grandson!

So Sheila took the advice of some local cowpokes and started off on something a mite smaller. Reckon she didn't know that the little fella was the second cousin removed of the bullock—and, boy, do these cattle stick together!

Ride 'im, cowgirl! Sheila was doin' real nicely till suddenly the little 'un began buckin' like a Brahma bull—

—and Sheila bit the dust, just like the Injuns do in them fancy films where the cavalry ride to the rescue at the last minute.

Well, I'll be doggone! Lookee here, folks—a good cowgirl never gives in, and now Sheila's doin' a mighty fine job. Even that mean critter reckons she's the pride of the prairie (Welsh style, o' course!).

MODEL MATCH

FOUR well-known fashion models appear below, separated from their outfits. Can you choose the right outfit for each model from clues given?

TEENAGE model TWIGGY has that little-girl look which enables her to look stunning in simple, young-looking styles. With her schoolgirl-type figure, she can wear frills and delicate materials — a style that needs no fussy accessories or jewellery to spoil its simplicity.

INTERNATIONAL star JEAN SHRIMPTON can wear any type of outfit with flair. With her tall, elegant figure, she looks marvellous in even the most demure dress with the minimum of trimmings.

A VERY "with-it" young model is SAMANTHA JUSTE, who goes for unusual styles, especially for evening wear. Stunning suits in one dazzling colour are top favourites in her wardrobe.

PATTI BOYD can wear outdoor clothes and striking evening clothes with equal flair. Girls with a slim figure like this model's, who can wear trouser suits successfully, have helped to launch this new-look fashion.

a   b   c   d

ANSWERS
(a) Patti Boyd.
(b) Jean Shrimpton.
(c) Samantha Juste.
(d) Twiggy.

THE GIRL WHO SETS THE STYLE—

MARY QUANT

MANY girls dream of rocketing to success in the fashion world. Few succeed—but one who did and went on to set the swing in British fashion is the young and talented, world-famous designer, Mary Quant, O.B.E.

AN ex-art student, Mary Quant began designing clothes by accident in her Chelsea bed-sitter. Then in 1955, along with her husband, Alexander Plunkett-Green, her first boutique, Bazaar, was opened in Chelsea.

TWO eye-catching outfits from one of Mary Quant's collections.

HERE is Mary and her husband who now helps her to run her vast international beauty and fashion business which has sprung up and made the name of Quant world famous. New collections appear every year, consisting of exciting and original designs.

A super mix and match outfit from Mary Quant's famous Ginger Group collection.

*I*N spite of her busy life, Mary Quant has still found time to write her autobiography, design rainwear, bags and launch a new range of cosmetics and scent.

Here, in her Chelsea flat, Mary looks for inspiration.

*I*N 1966, Mary Quant was mentioned in the Queen's Birthday Honours List and made an Officer of the Order of the British Empire. This distinction was awarded to her for her services to fashion.

*M*ARY QUANT has led the way for British fashion to set the style around the world.

Nurses OF TOMORROW'S WORLD

On May 12, 1820, a baby girl was born in Florence, Italy, who was to revolutionise the world of nursing. Her name was Florence Nightingale, a name which is known all over the world.

Miss Nightingale devoted her life to improving the standard of nursing, and it was largely due to her endeavours that standards in hospitals are so high today.

Nursing is now a highly honoured profession, and the girls shown here are being taught basic first-aid at their Junior Red Cross class. Any girls from eleven years upwards are eligible to join their local Cadet units, and the training given will prove of great value throughout their lives.

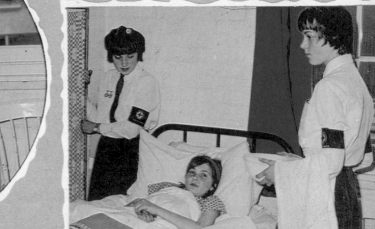

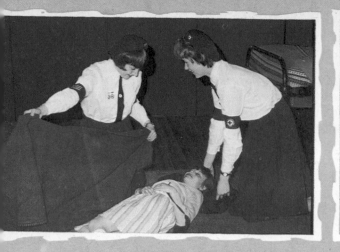

We are no Florence Nightingales,
    As you can plainly see,
But we enjoy our Red Cross class,
    Each Tuesday, after tea!

Bruises, sprains and headaches—
    Setting limbs in splints—
We know our stuff. We're full of
    Handy first-aid hints.

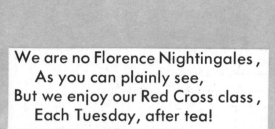

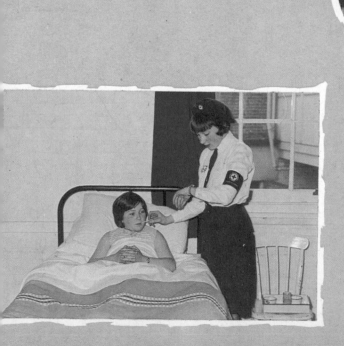

EMERGENCY NURSE GWEN

GWEN SANDERS is an Emergency Nurse at St Gilda's Hospital. Always on call, Gwen's job isn't easy —but she wouldn't change it for the world. However, one particular day, Gwen had been on the go from morning till night—

—and she was exhausted when she finally slumped into a chair in the nurses' rest room where a portrait of the famous Florence Nightingale hung on the wall.

> I'M SO TIRED I CAN HARDLY KEEP MY EYES OPEN.

Suddenly the room began to spin in a pink haze—and Gwen found herself near a battlefield taking orders from none other than Florence Nightingale. Wounded men lay sprawled out everywhere.

> TOO TIRED YOU SAY—I WON'T HEAR OF IT. THERE'S WORK TO BE DONE—SEE TO THE WOUNDED AT ONCE, AND HELP MOVE THEM TO THE HOSPITAL. THE CRIMEA IS NO PLACE FOR FAINT-HEARTED WEAKLINGS.

Gwen was back in the days of the Crimean War.

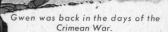

Gwen and the more able patients helped move the badly-wounded into the waiting wagons—

The hospital was no more than a ramshackle wooden hut— overcrowded and hopelessly short of medical supplies. But Gwen worked non-stop to bring comfort to the wounded soldiers.

At midday, a messenger brought alarming news.

> WATER, NURSE.

> I NEED CLEAN BANDAGES, NURSE.

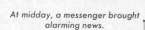

> YOU'LL HAVE TO MOVE OUT OF HERE AT ONCE, NURSES. THE RUSSIANS HAVE BROKEN OUR LINES —WE'RE IN RETREAT.

> THIS MAN IS TOO ILL TO BE MOVED. I'M STAYING HERE TO CARE FOR HIM.

Next morning, the Russian officer called on Gwen.

HOW IS YOUR PATIENT, ANGEL OF MERCY?

THE WORST OF HIS FEVER IS OVER—I THINK HE WILL LIVE.

GOOD! THEN HE CAN BE MOVED. I HAVE ARRANGED THAT YOU AND YOUR PATIENT BE GIVEN SAFE CONDUCT TO YOUR OWN PEOPLE. COURAGE SUCH AS YOURS IS AN INSPIRATION TO ALL OF US.

And so, Gwen and her patient returned to the British base hospital, and before long the soldier was well on the way to recovery.

I CAN NEVER REPAY YOU, FOR WHAT YOU HAVE DONE.

COME ALONG, NURSE—THERE'S MORE WORK TO BE DONE.

Florence Nightingale's order seemed to fade into the distance and Gwen awoke. She had been asleep, dreaming, back in the nurses' rest room at St Gilda's.

COME ALONG, NURSE—THERE'S MORE WORK TO BE DONE.

GOLLY—I MUST HAVE DROPPED OFF AND DREAMT I WAS BACK IN FLORENCE NIGHTINGALE'S TIME.

Emergency Nurse Gwen was taken to the scene of a road accident.

THIS BOY IS JUST LIKE THE YOUNG SOLDIER IN MY DREAM—THERE'S NO TIME TO FEEL TIRED—I MUST GO ON.

HELP ME, NURSE, HELP ME.

Some days later in hospital, the young man was out of danger.

MY DREAM CERTAINLY TAUGHT ME SOMETHING—A NURSE'S WORK IS NEVER DONE—AND I WOULDN'T HAVE IT ANY OTHER WAY.

THE BATTLING BADGER

AS the setting sun glinted on the waters of the River Tweed near Melrose, a black and white snout suddenly peeped out from a hole amongst the roots of an oak tree. It was Stripey the badger coming out into his dark world of the night.

First Stripey chewed up some green shoots, then scraped up some bluebell bulbs and gulped them down.

Next on Stripey's menu was a young rabbit, dug out from its burrow by the badger's razor-sharp claws.

After his meal, Stripey returned to his sett, an underground wonderland of tunnels and caves carved out by generations of badgers over a period of fifty years.

Stripey wasn't the only resident in the underground maze. In a far corner, a fox and his vixen were raising a family of three cubs.

STRIPEY had been born in that sett two years before. He was one of three cubs and his father wasted no time in gathering leaves and moss to make comfortable fresh bedding for his family.

Stripey and his brothers liked nothing better than when their mother nosed them through the woods to their very own private playground.

The playground was a tiny clearing in the woods, free from the carpet of dead leaves. There the young badgers puffed up their fur till they looked like little footballs—then they jumped, tumbled and nipped each other in their own crazy game of leap-frog.

That autumn Stripey moved away from his parents' chamber and dug out his own compartment in the sett.

Once he had dug out his site, he lined it with fresh chestnut leaves and dried grass tufts. Yes, Stripey liked his comfort.

It was in that compartment that Stripey took a mate and raised his own family. He was a fine father who didn't spare himself to see that his family had the best of everything.

One night Stripey took his cubs to their playground, then left them to forage for some food. He knew the youngsters would be hungry after their hectic frolicking.

But, while Stripey was gone, an enemy picked up the scent of the badger cubs. Moving menacingly towards the clearing was a powerful dog otter from the river.

Ravenously hungry, the otter sprang at one of the chubby cubs.

But Stripey was not far away and he heard the shrill screams of panic.

Stripey charged towards the clearing as fast as his legs would carry him—then threw himself savagely at the otter, who was forced to release the cub.

The fight was on. Badger and otter rolled over and over in a tangle of fur. Stripey's claws ripped and gouged, while the otter tried to sink its teeth into Stripey's soft snout.

But a swift slash of Stripey's claw ripped into the otter's chest—and, weakened from the loss of blood, the otter fled from the clearing. Stripey had won and his family were safe.

Stripey watched the otter flee. He didn't follow. A badger fights not for blood-lust — only for defence. Once again Stripey had proved himself an ideal father!

the ONE LEGGED EAGLE

Suddenly, he spotted a movement further down the mountainside. The movement was slight, but Corra knew at once it was a mountain hare.

CORRA, the golden eagle, banked and circled a thousand feet above the summit of Ben Macdhui, in Scotland. The magnificent eagle was scanning his territory, searching keenly for his evening meal.

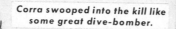

Corra swooped into the kill like some great dive-bomber.

Even the fantastic speed of the hare couldn't shake off the hungry eagle—and soon Corra was rising into the air with his prey clutched in his one powerful talon.

The eagle carried the dead hare to his eyrie—which was built on a narrow ledge about 2000 feet up Ben Macdhui.

An eagle's nest is an amazing construction of sticks, twigs and boughs, lined with heather and moss, all woven together to withstand the fierce mountain winds.

IT was in this self-same eyrie that Corra had been born, with sound lungs and a sharp set of talons.

The baby Corra had been a gawky young chick, always greedy to gobble up any tit-bits which his hard-working father brought home.

As the weeks passed, Corra grew stronger—and one day he stood up in the nest and beat his scraggy wings defiantly at the drop beneath him.

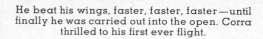

He beat his wings, faster, faster, faster—until finally he was carried out into the open. Corra thrilled to his first ever flight.

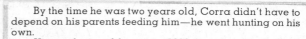

By the time he was two years old, Corra didn't have to depend on his parents feeding him—he went hunting on his own.

Up, up he would soar to 5000 feet — carried along effortlessly in the strong currents of warm air that rose from the glens below.

Then he would come in to land on some craggy cliff-top, his restless eyes ever seeking out food—mostly hares, rabbits and game birds.

Corra had learned to beat the heather with his wings to flush out the plump birds from their hiding-places.

When he was five years old, Corra took a mate — and they began to build their giant nest high on the cliff rocks, above Loch Torridon in Ross-shire.

The following spring, Corra became the proud father of two golden eagle chicks—and that meant extra food had to be found.

One morning, Corra spotted the lifeless body of a hare—this was too easy—

But the dead hare was a decoy set for a fox, and the cruel jaws of the steel trap beside the hare bit into Corra's leg. He tried to soar, but the chain of the trap was attached to the dry-stane dyke.

Corra knew that if he didn't return with food, his chicks would die—so he bit through his trapped claw with his razor-sharp beak—

One swift stroke and the claw was left in the trap. But Corra was free! Crippled, but game, Corra flew off with the dead hare to feed his chicks.

Corra soon forgot his crippled leg—it made only one difference—from now on, with only one talon, he would have to attack very young and defenceless prey.

Yes, Corra was still a magnif golden eagle — monarch o Scottish skies!

TWO STRANGE WOMEN

THE SPHINX

THE oldest sphinx is HARMAKHIS, the Great Sphinx of Gizeh, near Cairo. With the pyramids it guards, it was one of the Seven Wonders of the Ancient World, and it is still one of the most famous monuments of all time.

It was sculptured out of solid rock over 5000 years ago, on the orders of the ruling Pharaoh, King Khephren, who sited it in front of his pyramid tomb. Its head was a portrait of the Pharaoh, but he gave it the body and the paws of a lion to show that he was a strong ruler and was protecting his people and land.

The Great Sphinx is 66 feet high and 187 feet long, and the Pharaoh's face is in proportion. It is 14 feet wide and measures 19 feet from the top of the forehead to the tip of the chin.

In spite of its colossal size, the Sphinx has often been buried by the sand. When the Egyptian authorities had all the sand cleared away in 1926, they discovered an open-air temple between the great paws. At one time it had obviously been worshipped as a sun god or goddess.

THE wind and the sand have altered the features. According to the ancient travellers, the Sphinx had a graceful smile, but today, particularly when it is floodlit in the evenings, the smile is strange and mysterious. One can understand why the Arabs call it "The Creator of Terrors" and why the simile, "as inscrutable as the smile on the face of the Sphinx" is world-wide.

Other Pharaohs after Khephren built sphinxes and for thousands of years they continued to be royal portraits of the Egyptian rulers. None is as large as the Great Sphinx and most are only nine feet long. But all of them bear the head of a past king.

From Egypt the idea of the sphinx spread throughout the ancient world. The Greeks made it a monster instead of a portrait statue. They gave it the face and bust of a woman and added the wings of a bird to its lion's body. They also believed that it was omniscient—that it knew all the answers. Even today, the wisdom of the sphinx is proverbial.

THE most famous of the Greek sphinxes guarded the road to the city of Thebes. It was the offspring of two giants and lived on human flesh. It stopped all travellers and asked them a riddle, devouring those who could not give the right answer.

When the crown of Thebes was promised to anyone who could free the city from this monster, Oedipus decided to attempt the feat. The sphinx asked him, "Which is the animal that has four feet in the morning, two at midday, and three in the evening?"

Oedipus answered, "Man, who in infancy crawls on all fours, who walks upright on two feet in maturity, and in his old age supports himself with a stick."

The sphinx was vanquished and in her anger threw herself over the cliffs into the sea and was drowned. Thebes was saved and Oedipus became king.

THE OLD LADY OF THREADNEEDLE STREET

SHE is one of the oldest and most respected women in the world. She has lasted for 271 years and will undoubtedly carry on for many years yet. She is the Bank of England, whose main building is in Threadneedle Street in the heart of the City of London.

The Bank was founded in 1694 by William Paterson, who arranged a loan of £1,200,000 for William III. William urgently needed money to wage war against France, and in return for the loan gave the Bank a charter and the right to issue banknotes. Over the years it became very powerful and now acts as the banker for the Government and the commercial banks. It was nationalised in 1946, and its Governor and Directors are appointed by the Government.

It is the only English bank allowed to print and issue notes and an engraving of Britannia—the Old Lady herself —has appeared on every one of its notes since 1694. You will see her on the back of a pound or ten shilling note, holding her trident and shield.

If you turn the note over you will see the legend

BANK OF ENGLAND

I promise to pay the Bearer on Demand the sum of

For the Gov. and Comp. of the Bank of England

Chief Cashier

This is a relic of the days before the First World War when all Bank of England notes could be exchanged on demand for an equivalent sum in gold. Now the notes are inconvertible and the promise to pay is meaningless.

THE simile, "as safe as the Bank of England", is a reminder that the Bank has never been robbed. No doubt many criminals have dreamed of breaking in and stealing some of the gold from its vaults, but none has succeeded. It is said that in 1836 the Directors received a letter from a man who said that he knew a way of breaking in and he arranged to meet them in the vault on a certain night. The Directors gathered there and up he came through the floorboards. He was a labourer who had found a way in while repairing some old sewers. He was given £800 as a reward for his honesty. Those of you who have seen the film, "The Day They Robbed the Bank of England", will remember that the gang got in by means of an old sewer!

During the Gordon Riots of 1780 the mob attacked the Bank and the Government sent soldiers to protect it. Ever since then there has been a permanent nightly guard of twelve Guardsmen, led by an officer, a sergeant, two corporals and a piper or drummer. A guard is not really necessary today as there are all kinds of burglar alarms and many civilian watchmen. But, like every old lady, the Bank of England likes to keep up the traditions.

For nearly two centuries the piquet's nightly march through the streets of London has been a favourite attraction for visitors. Long may it continue!

HAVE FUN WITH FACTS

OCTOBER QUIZ?

Can you fill in the blanks in the following important October events?

Date	Year	Event.
2	1452	King Richard III was born. He was suspected of murdering the princes in the Tower to gain the throne and was killed at the Battle of . . . . in 1485 after Henry Tudor raised a rebellion against him.
3	1226	Saint Francis of Assissi died. After serving as a soldier, he decided to live a life of poverty and preach a simple Christian faith. He founded an order of friars known as the . . . .
6	1820	Jenny Lind was born at Stockholm. She was a famous singer, and because of the rich tones of her voice was called the Swedish . . . .
7	1571	The Battle of Lepanto. In this famous naval battle the Christian forces under Don John of Austria inflicted a crushing defeat on the Turks. Cervantes, who later wrote . . . . , fought in one of the Spanish ships.
8	1754	Henry Fielding, the English novelist, died. His most famous novel, ... , was made into a film two years ago, with Albert Finney in the leading role.
10	1877	Lord Nuffield, the motor car manufacturer and philanthropist, was born. His first large factory was at Cowley, near Oxford, where he began the mass production of . . . . cars.
12	1492	Land was first sighted by Columbus on his voyage to the West to reach Asia. It was probably Watling Island that he saw and, after landing on it, he sailed on to discover Cuba and Haiti. This day is celebrated in the United States as . . . . Day.
12	1915	Nurse Edith Cavell was shot by the Germans for helping English and French soldiers to escape from Belgium to Holland. At her trial she said, ". . . . ."

14	1066	The Battle of Hastings. The Normans under . . . . defeated King Harold of England, who was killed in the battle.
16	1793	Marie Antoinette, the widow of Louis XVI, was guillotined by the French revolutionaries for treason. She was an . . . . and was accused of betraying the French plans to her country, which was at war with France.
17	1849	Frederic Chopin, the Polish composer and pianist, died. He wrote many sonatas, mazurkas, nocturnes, &c. Most of his works are solos for the . . . .
19	1745	Jonathan Swift, the author and satirist, died. His most famous book is ". . . . ." about the adventures of a ship's surgeon in a number of imaginary countries.
20	1842	Grace Darling died. She was the daughter of a lighthouse keeper, and when the *Forfarshire* was wrecked off the Farne Islands in 1838, she rowed with her father to the wreck and saved . . . . men.
21	1772	Samuel Taylor Coleridge, the poet, was born. Perhaps his best-known poem is "The Rime of the . . . ."
22	1845	Sarah Bernhardt was born in Paris. She was the most famous actress of her day and was known as "The . . . . Sarah."
25	1854	The Charge of the Light Brigade in the Crimean War. This is described in a poem by . . . .
28	1886	The Statue of Liberty was unveiled by President Cleveland. The statue was a gift from France to the U.S.A. and stands on a small island in . . . . harbour.
30	1910	Jean Henri Dunant died. After seeing the plight of the wounded at the Battle of Solferino he founded the International Red Cross. In Moslem countries the emblem is a . . . . instead of a cross.
31	every year	. . . . , the evening before All Saints Day, when you bob for apples and make turnip lanterns.

ANSWERS:—

IS YOUR NAME SMITH?

HAVE you ever wondered how you got your surname? If you had lived seven or eight hundred years ago, you probably would not have had one. It was not until the Middle Ages, when the population began to increase and people began to move about more, that it became necessary to distinguish between one Mary and another.

A surname was not at one time a sire name—the name given by a father to his children — as many people believe. "Sur" means additional, and a surname was the additional name added to a child's given or Christian name. Very often, children's surnames were different from their father's.

LET'S imagine that a man called William lived in the 14th century and was the village smith. A smith's main work was shoeing horses and making weapons and ploughshares; he worked with metal or "smited". William was a good workman, and by the time he had six sons (not unusual in those days) he had become known as William Smith. He let his wife, Mary, choose the Christian names, and she called them Robert, William (after Dad), John, Richard, Henry and Stephen.

Robert, the eldest, went to work with his father and became known as Robert Smith. William, to distinguish him from his father, was called Young William and, later, William Young. John, as a son of William, became William's son or Williamson. Richard was apprenticed to a mason and eventually became Richard Mason. Henry, who was always growing out of his clothes, became so tall that he was nicknamed Longshanks—and the nickname stuck. Stephen, when he married left home, went to live in a hut on the hill and gradually became Stephen Hill.

It took generations, of course, before surnames became fixed and children were always called after their father. But this little story does illustrate five of the main ways in which surnames originated. They are by occupation (Smith and Mason); status or social standing (Young); family relationship (Williamson); physical characteristics (Longshanks); and place of residence (Hill).

THE commonest surnames come from occupations— Baker, Butcher, Taylor, Farmer, Miller, Wright, Goldsmith, and so on. Smith, incidentally, is the most common name in Europe as well as in Britain. In France it is Ferrier, in Spain Herrero, in Italy Ferraro, in Germany Schmidt and, wait for it, in Russia Kusnetsov.

Surnames going back to social standing include Elder, Younger, Squire, Baron, Knight, King, Priest, Marquis and Pope. By the way, if your name is King, don't preen yourself because you have royal blood in your veins. It's much more likely that your ancestor was called this because he played the part of a king in a morality play or pageant!

Family relationships? All those names ending in "son" and many ending in "s", like Harris, which was originally Harrison, Parsons—once the parson's son, and Jones which was Jone's son, "Jone" being the early spelling of John. Fitz, Mac, Mc and O', as in Fitzgerald, MacTavish, McDowell and O'Neill, all mean "son of".

IN 1235, the Moors occupied the southern part of Spain, but raiding parties still pushed their way north into the part of Spain that was still Christian.

A CHRISTMAS MIRACLE

On the morning of December 24th, at the convent of the Carmelite nuns at Santa Cruz—

AH, SISTERS, BRING THE MODEL FIGURES TO THE FOOT OF THE ALTAR.

The nuns were arranging figures representing the Nativity scene. With them was their chaplain, Father Bruno.

WHAT A LOVELY SURPRISE THIS WILL BE FOR OUR DEAR MOTHER SUPERIOR.

Just then, the Mother Superior appeared—

SISTER FLORA! PLAYING WITH DOLLS AT YOUR AGE!

EXCUSE ME, MOTHER, BUT IT WAS SUGGESTED BY FATHER BRUNO.

WHAT? OUR CHAPLAIN?

YES, REVEREND MOTHER, IT WAS OUR FOUNDER, FRANCIS OF ASSISI, WHO FIRST THOUGHT OF A NATIVITY SCENE.

I MUST SAY IT'S A CHARMING IDEA!

But as the nuns prepared for Christmas, a few miles away, a band of Moors had gathered.

TONIGHT THE CHRISTIANS CELEBRATE A BIG FEAST. THE NUNS AT SANTA CRUZ WILL NO DOUBT DISPLAY THEIR PRECIOUS ORNAMENTS.

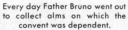
Every day Father Bruno went out to collect alms on which the convent was dependent.

On his way through the countryside, Father Bruno met a man on horseback.

But that evening, Father Bruno met up with the Moorish raiders.

The Moors pulled out a chicken and the precious gold ring given to the monk for the convent.

That evening, at the nearby village of Orfila, Count d'Orgaz halted his journey.

Leaving the town behind, the Count spurred on his horse.

THEY INTEND TO RAID THE CONVENT THEN IF I GO THROUGH THE OLIVE GROVE I CAN REACH SANTA CRUZ FIRST

I HOPE TO HEAVEN I'M NOT TOO LATE

The Count arrived at the convent before the Moors.

SISTER, THE MOORS ARE NOW ON THEIR WAY HERE. YOU MAY HAVE A VISIT FROM THEM.

NO MAN IS ALLOWED TO ENTER THE CLOISTER. BUT YOU MAY STAY IN THE HOSTEL OUTSIDE.

HOW CAN I HELP TO PROTECT YOU AGAINST ALL THOSE MOORS?

IT WOULD BE WISE TO BOLT THE ENTRANCE DOOR.

BUT OUR CHAPLAIN, FATHER BRUNO, HASN'T RETURNED.

The Mother Superior gathered the nuns together in the chapel and explained their dangerous situation.

KEEP CALM, DEAR SISTERS, WE ARE IN THE HANDS OF GOD.

But everyone seemed to have forgotten the young novice, Sister Flora, who was outside the walls of the convent tending her flowers.

When Mother Superior found the young novice—

MY DEAR CHILD, YOU FACE GREAT DANGER OUT HERE.

I HAVE BEEN READY TO FACE DEATH, MOTHER, FOR A LONG TIME.

I HAVE IMPLORED MY FLOWERS TO INTERCEDE WITH THE CHILD JESUS FOR THE SAFETY OF THE CONVENT.

SUCH AN INNOCENT SOUL.

Soon the Moorish raiders appeared—

IF YOU DON'T OPEN UP, WE WILL BREAK DOWN THE DOOR.

ALL WE WANT IS YOUR TREASURE.

IF YOU RESIST, YOU WILL BE PUT TO THE SWORD AND THE BUILDING BURNT.

BE ON YOUR WAY!

LEAVE US IN PEACE!

The Moors tried to batter the door down, but with no success.

LUCKY FOR YOU THE DOOR IS SOLID. WE WILL FETCH LADDERS AND ATTACK AT DAWN.

HA! I SHALL NEVER LEAVE HERE—UNLESS MY SWORD TAKES ROOT IN THE GROUND.

COME, MY DAUGHTERS, WE MUST PREPARE TO DIE AT DAWN.

At dawn, Moorish reinforcements arrived with ladders to scale the walls of the convent.

When the leader of the Moors went to pull his scimitar from the ground, he found it was held fast by a flower which was growing round the blade —as if by magic.

IT'S UNBELIEVABLE! MY SWORD HAS BEEN TRAPPED BY A FLOWER. QUICKLY! WE MUST LEAVE AT ONCE.

But at that moment, the Count, who had been in hiding, appeared before the Moorish leader.

THE BATTLE IS NOT OVER YET, EMIR.

Father Bruno, a prisoner of the Moors, uttered a silent prayer.

I CHALLENGE YOU TO FIGHT FOR THE FREEDOM OF YOUR PRISONER.

SO BE IT!

After a swift and furious battle, the defeated Moor lay dead at the feet of the brave Count d'Orgaz and Father Bruno was released by the Moors.

YOU ARE A BRAVE AND JUST MAN.

The defeated Moors rode swiftly away.

I CAN'T UNDERSTAND IT! IT WAS LIKE A MIRACLE.

IT WAS A YOUNG NOVICE'S LOVE OF FLOWERS THAT SAVED US, FATHER.

And so the nuns were left in peace to celebrate Christmas and thank the Infant Saviour for their salvation.

THE MAGIC MIRROR

HUH! EVEN SANTA CLAUS FORGOT ABOUT ME HIDDEN AWAY IN THIS OLD ATTIC. NOT AS MUCH AS A SNOW-FLAKE IN MY STOCKING!

MAGGIE MEADE, the little maid-of-all-work in a strange old country house, finds a Magic Mirror amongst a heap of junk in her attic bedroom.

The Mirror flashes at the most unexpected moments and changes to a magic doorway through which Maggie can walk and go back in time.

One day, not long after Christmas—

Maggie rummaged round the attic in an effort to find some knick-knack to cheer her up.

HOOPEE! WHAT A FIND! [SOM]E XMAS CRACKERS THAT [WE]NT PULLING! I'LL SOON SEE TO THAT.

So—KERACK—Maggie pulled one of the crackers—

—and out of it came a small piece of paper.

HM—A RECIPE FOR CHRISTMAS PUDDING. NOW IF I ONLY HAD THE INGREDIENTS.

CHRISTMAS PUDDING

CANDIED PEEL 2 ozs.
CURRANTS
RAISINS
TREACLE
FLOUR
SPICE

OH! OH! HERE WE GO AGAIN! LET'S SEE WHERE I LAND THIS TIME.

Her mouth watering at the thought of the Christmas pudding, Maggie was irresistibly drawn towards the Magic Mirror, which had suddenly begun to flash in a mysterious way. She was still clutching the box of crackers.

Through the mirror and back into time went Maggie—to find herself in the sixteenth century on board a galleon ploughing through a heavy sea.

GOLLY! I WISH THEY'D STOP ROCKING THE BOAT. I DON'T SUPPOSE THEY'VE ANY SEA-SICKNESS PILLS EITHER. THEY HAVEN'T BEEN INVENTED YET, I DON'T SUPPOSE.

PYONG! Suddenly, a dagger thrown by a hairy Highlander flashed into the mast inches above Maggie's head.

AH! WATCH WHAT YOU'RE DOING WITH YOUR CUTLERY, YOU HAGGIS BASHER.

Maggie was dragged below decks, where she was amazed to see Mary Queen of Scots and her four attendants — the famous Four Marys.

I THINK WE HAVE AN ENGLISH SPY ON BOARD, YOUR MAJESTY.

Mary was on her way from France to Scotland to claim the Scottish throne. Her husband, the French Dauphin, was not long dead. It was the year 1561.

IT IS WITH A HEAVY HEART THAT I GO TO SCOTLAND. BUT TELL ME —ARE YOU A SPY, YOUNG LASS?

I'M NO SPY—AND TO CHEER YOU UP, I'LL SHARE A CHRISTMAS CRACKER WITH YOU.

But the sad queen declined.

WELL HOW ABOUT THIS, THEN? A RECIPE FOR CHRISTMAS PUDDING. IF YOU HAVE THE INGREDIENTS ABOARD, I WILL MAKE IT FOR YOU.

WHAT A DELICIOUS SWEETMEAT—YES, GO AHEAD AND PREPARE IT.

Later, a look-out on an English patrol ship spotted Queen Mary's galleon.

AHOY THERE! A SHIP BEARING DOWN ON US.

FORSOOTH—'TIS A FRENCH GALLEON—PREPARE TO DO BATTLE—MAN THE GUNS.

Soon the two ships were engaged in a furious battle.

But Maggie was too busy preparing her Christmas pudding to notice.

On deck, Mary talked with her captain.

YOU'LL HAVE TO SURRENDER—THIS SHIP HASN'T THE SPEED OR THE GUN POWER OF THE ENGLISH SHIP.

IF YOU SAY SO, YOUR MAJESTY. I WOULDN'T RISK YOUR LIFE—BUT LET'S GIVE THEM ONE MORE BROADSIDE.

The captain was hearing some bad news as Maggie appeared on deck proudly carrying the steaming plum duff.

YOU CAN FORGET ABOUT THAT BROADSIDE. WE'RE OUT OF AMMUNITION. NOT AS MUCH AS A MARBLE LEFT, CAP'N.

Just then, the ship pitched—and SPLODGE—Maggie's pudding rolled off its plate and trundled along the deck.

STOP THAT PUDDING!

Before Maggie could reach the pudding, it reached a gun crew who mistook it for a cannon ball.

PHEW! THESE CANNON-BALLS GET HEAVIER ALL THE TIME.

OF ALL THE NERVE! THAT'S MY PUDDING HE'S TALKING ABOUT!

Just Hanging Around

How marvellous to be a puppet on a string! I mean—no worries, no lessons, no homework. Just a show once every evening—and it's the puppets that get the applause—not the puppeteers!

JUST MY LUCK! THESE WOODEN-HEADED COPS ARE EVERYWHERE. BUT THE STUFF IS SAFE—AS LONG AS HE DOESN'T UNSCREW MY LEFT FOOT...

SMUGGLER, EH? IT'S NOT ALL FUN IN THE PUPPET WORLD! NEVER MIND, I'LL TIE HIM UP IN HIS OWN STRINGS!

NO, IT'S NO GREAT SHAKES BEING A PUPPET— DANCING AROUND WHENEVER SOMEBODY PULLS THE STRINGS.

THE SOCIAL LIFE IS A DRAG, TOO. THE WORST THING IS ALL THIS HANGING AROUND!

The First PUNCH and JUDY MAN

Near the end of the 18th century in France, a crisis arose in the silk-weaving city of Lyons.

IT'S NO USE STANDING THERE. THE FACTORY HAS CLOSED DOWN.

WHAT'S GOING TO HAPPEN TO US?

I AM SORRY, MY FRIENDS, BUT THERE IS NO MORE WORK FOR YOU.

Among the workmen out of a job was one Laurent Mourguet.

THIS IS A NICE MESS WE'RE IN.

ALREADY A THIRD OF THE SILK-WEAVERS OF LYONS ARE OUT OF WORK, LAURENT.

Laurent went straight home.

WHY ARE YOU HOME SO EARLY?

THE SILK FACTORY HAS PAID OFF ALL ITS WORKERS.

BUT WE'VE HARDLY ENOUGH TO LIVE ON FOR THE REST OF THE WEEK!

I'LL SOON FIND ANOTHER JOB.

But Laurent found that other work was hard to come by.

IT'S NO USE PERSISTING— WE ALREADY HAVE A BOY TO RUN MESSAGES.

I AM STRONG, SIR. I COULD CARRY THE BUILDING MATERIALS.

I TELL YOU I HAVE ALL THE MEN I NEED.

That evening—

WHY IS THE CHILD CRYING, MARIE?

BECAUSE SHE'S HUNGRY, POOR LITTLE THING.

DON'T CRY, RAFALIE...COME ON, PAPA WILL PLAY WITH YOU.

Next day, in the park—

But admission to the puppet show was 3 sous—far more than the Mourguets could afford.

But the puppets gave Laurent an idea!

Several hours later—

Courageously, Laurent and his friend went on carving other characters.

I HOPE THIS WILL WORK OUT.

IT MUST! I HAVEN'T A SOU LEFT.

That very day—

YOUR RENT IS NOW OVERDUE, MOURGUET!

IT IS BECAUSE I HAVE BEEN OUT OF WORK FOR TWO WEEKS, AND...

ENOUGH! IF I DO NOT RECEIVE MY MONEY WITHIN 48 HOURS, THE BAILIFFS WILL TURN YOU OUT!

WITH SUCH A GREEDY LANDLORD, THERE IS NO HOPE FOR US.

WE'RE NOT FINISHED YET. WE'LL WORK ALL NIGHT.

So, next day, in the densely-populated area on the banks of the Rhone—

I HOPE YOU WILL READ OUT THE STORY OF ACTION.

YOU ARE A GOOD STORY TELLER. DO IT AS YOU WORK THE PUPPETS.

WELL, HERE GOES— IT'S DO OR DIE!

TODAY AT 3 P.M. FIRST PERFORMANCE of the PUNCH AND JUDY THEATRE ADMISSION 1 SOU

DON'T MISS THIS WONDERFUL NEW ENTERTAINMENT!

At three o'clock—

HOW IS IT GOING?

ONLY TWELVE PEOPLE HAVE COME. IT IS MOST DISCOURAGING.

It was to that tiny audience that Punch and Judy made their debuts.

More and more people began to flock in.

By the end of the performance—

Thanks to the courage and energy of their inventor, Punch and Judy went on to win great popularity.

After 1818, Laurent Mourguet, helped by Rafalie and by his son-in-law, ran the first Punch and Judy Theatre in Paris.

What actor could boast of such continuing popularity as the "Punch and Judy" characters who began in Lyons two centuries ago?

MAKE YOUR OWN PUPPET THEATRE
starring–
THE GIRLS from N.O.O.D.L.E.S.

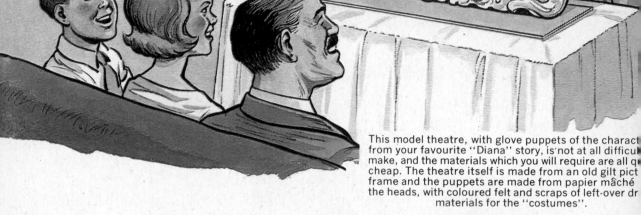

This model theatre, with glove puppets of the charact[ers] from your favourite "Diana" story, is not at all difficul[t to] make, and the materials which you will require are all q[uite] cheap. The theatre itself is made from an old gilt pict[ure] frame and the puppets are made from papier mâché [for] the heads, with coloured felt and scraps of left-over dr[ess] materials for the "costumes".

GALE

NICOLA

The basic glove-puppet body is made from two pieces of coloured felt (the thin grade) cut to the shape which you see at the right, and sewn together. The decorative white lines on the costumes of GALE and NICOLA are made from strips of white felt either stitched on or stuck on with fabric glue. Costume details for the other characters, like the waistcoat of the man with the eye-patch, are easily made from scraps of colourful material.

8¾"

2"

2¼"

5⅛"

6¼"

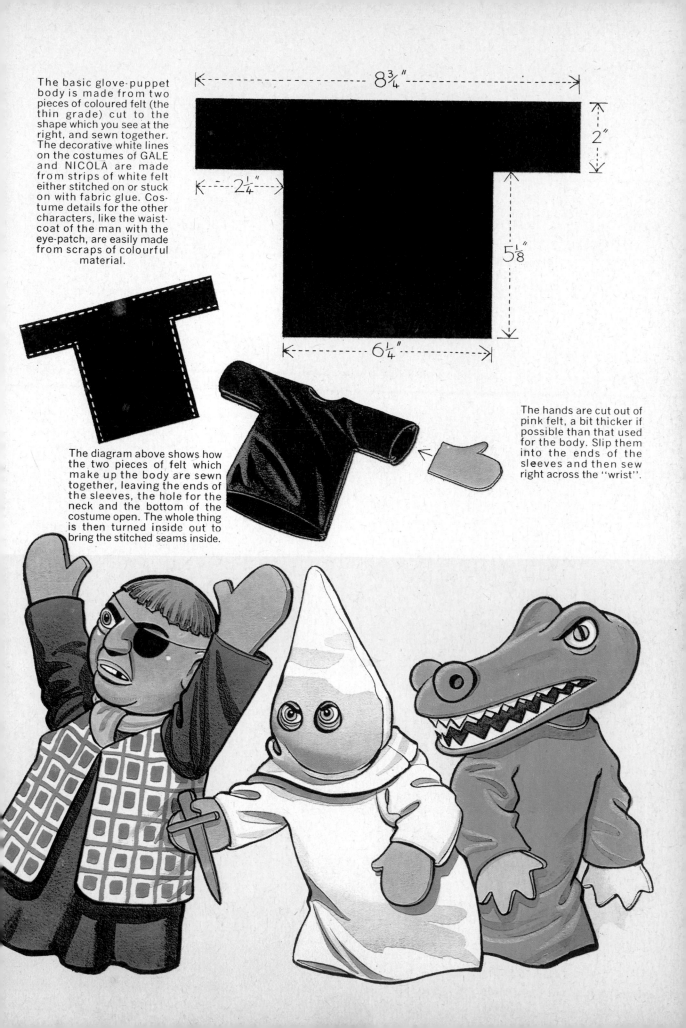

The diagram above shows how the two pieces of felt which make up the body are sewn together, leaving the ends of the sleeves, the hole for the neck and the bottom of the costume open. The whole thing is then turned inside out to bring the stitched seams inside.

The hands are cut out of pink felt, a bit thicker if possible than that used for the body. Slip them into the ends of the sleeves and then sew right across the "wrist".

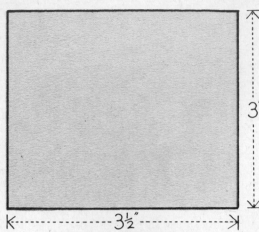

In making the head, the first thing to do is to cut a piece of thin card into a rectangle 3 in. x 3½ in. A piece of postcard is ideal. Now wrap this piece of card LOOSELY round your middle finger to make a tube like the one at the right, and join it with a strip of cellulose tape. Now you are ready to start modelling with papier mâché, and if you do not already know how to make this material you will find instructions in the panel at the bottom of this page.

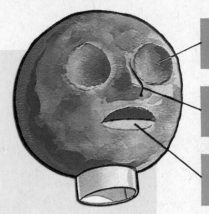

Press with thumbs to make eye-sockets.

Pinch-up papier mache between finger and thumb to start nose.

Press in edge of ruler here to start making mouth.

First you must build up a ball of papier mâché on the tube of card, leaving some of the card sticking out at the bottom for the neck. Build up the ball in several layers, running the paste brush over the surface in between layers. The papier mache should not be too sloppy—just wet enough to hold together.

Now you can model the head up completely. Make two small balls of papier mâché for the eyes, then run the paste brush lightly over the eye sockets and press the "eye-balls" firmly into the sockets. Model the nose and lips, using the pointed end of a paintbrush handle or some similar point as a modelling tool. You may have to add some small pieces of papier mâché to make the tip and sides of the nose and to fill out the lips. Poke small holes for the nostrils with a pencil point.

When the head is completely modelled, put it aside to dry for several hours—preferably overnight. A warm airing cupboard is a good place in which to do this, but not an oven, which would probably be too warm and would cause the model to shrink too quickly and crack.

When it is quite dry, you can paint the head with poster colours. Finally, add the hair, which is made of wool teazled out and brushed and then stuck to the top of the head with a dab of balsa cement or similar glue.

HOW TO MAKE PAPIER MÂCHÉ

You will require some old newspapers, a large bowl and some cold-water paste. You can buy the paste in powder form at hardware shops or wallpaper shops. The instructions for mixing it are on the packet.

Tear up several sheets of newspaper into small pieces —pieces about the size of a shilling—and place them in a bowl of water. Leave them there to soak for at least a day. When the paper is really thoroughly soaked, pound it well with a thick stick until it goes pulpy. Now take it out of the water a handful at a time and squeeze most of the water out of it. When you have treated all the paper-pulp in this way, empty the water out of the bowl and put the squeezed-out pulp back into it. Now mix cold-water paste with the pulp a little at a time until it makes a sticky mass which you can model with. It should be neither too wet nor too dry.

The head of the ALLIGATOR is just a bit more difficult than the ordinary heads, as it has to have the long jaws built on to it. To make these, first cut out two pieces of postcard shaped like the pattern at the right. They should be about four inches long. Then score along the dotted lines and fold the rows of "teeth" down to make the jaw-shapes.

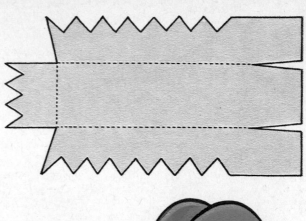

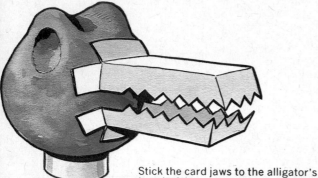

Stick the card jaws to the alligator's head with paste while the papier mâché of the head is still damp. You can then model the top and bottom of the jaws with papier mâché over the card, leaving the teeth uncovered.

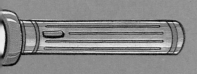

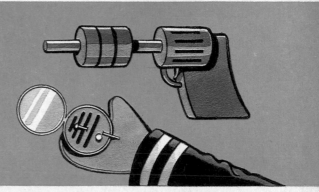

en you are acting out the stories from "Diana" with your puppets, u will need certain "props" from time to time, like those shown in this nel. These can either be painted on card and cut out or made out of all pieces of balsa wood which is very easy to carve with a sharp knife. ey are attached to the hands of the puppets as required simply by pinning them on as you see in the picture at the right.

Here you see a picture of the back view of the "theatre", showing you how it is made. As you see, it is simply an old picture frame (as ornate and gilded as you can get) attached to a plywood base. You then make the curtains from a suitable remnant of material and hang them from an ordinary expanding curtain wire. Old picture frames can usually be picked up from a saleroom or a junk shop for a shilling or two—sometimes for nothing!

CURTAIN WIRE

PLYWOOD BASE

METAL ANGLE-BRACKETS SCREWED TO PICTURE-FRAME AND BASE

DIANA'S SPECIAL SECTION OF GIRLS ON THE GO

GO GO GO GO GO GO

Girls on the go—off to tackle unusual jobs, jobs that take very special talents. Girls in a hurry—living in a fast-moving world—keeping up with the times. Girls ON THE GO!

GO GO GO GO GO GO GO GO GO GO GO GO GO

There's a girl for every job,
A job for every girl—
Except for some like Dilly Dream,
Who's always in a whirl.

No matter what she tries to do,
She'll always get it wrong!
But not to worry, she'll soon find
Where Dilly Dreams belong . . .

BUT WHAT ABOUT ME?

Patrolette

Here's a job for a girl who likes to be really "on the move". Each R.A.C. Patrolette has a smart uniform, a super motor scooter and a fascinating variety of duties. She has to know all about the services the R.A.C. offers to motorists, and often a course in First-Aid is included in her training programme.

Patrolettes visit members in their homes to discuss their motoring problems, act as guides at displays, exhibitions and sports events, and staff these cute little caravans (mobile offices) you see dotted here and there on our roads.

A job for a girl who knows where she's going—and how to get there and back!

What about a Very Important Job in the magic world of the theatre?

Wardrobe

The main duties of a Wardrobe Mistress are to see that the costumes are kept clean and in good shape for each production. Of course, the bigger the cast, the harder the job!

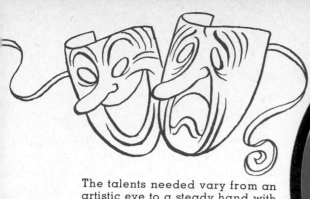

The talents needed vary from an artistic eye to a steady hand with a needle!

Mistress

On really big occasions, like "first nights", a wardrobe mistress is especially busy, for all the costumes must be really in tip-top condition. It's a satisfying job, looking after the costumes of the stars. It's a job for a handy girl—with a cool head!

Zoo Girl

Do you like animals? Then how about a zoo job? Some zoos employ girls as keepers, especially in the children's sections.

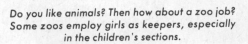

You might not have much to do with the big cats, but lots of smaller fry will want you to make a fuss of them, and will depend on you for their comforts.

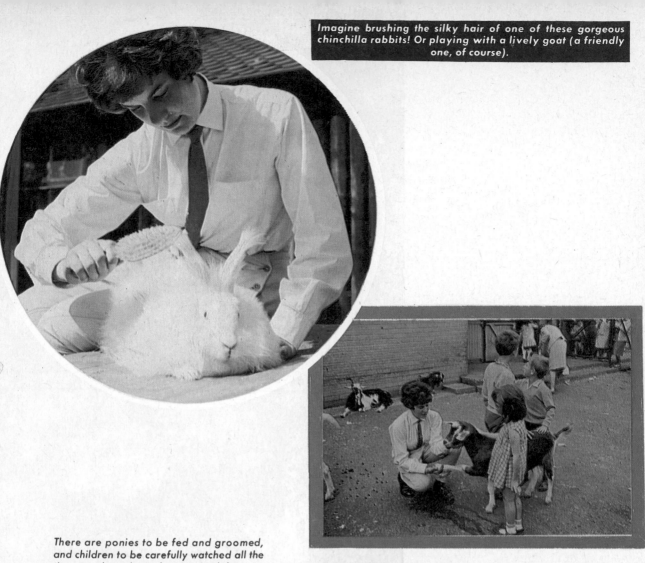

There are ponies to be fed and groomed, and children to be carefully watched all the time—and you know how excited they can get when they're surrounded by lots and lots of animals! It's a job for a girl who doesn't mind being on the run all day long!

IS THIS THE BEST THEY CAN DO FOR ME?

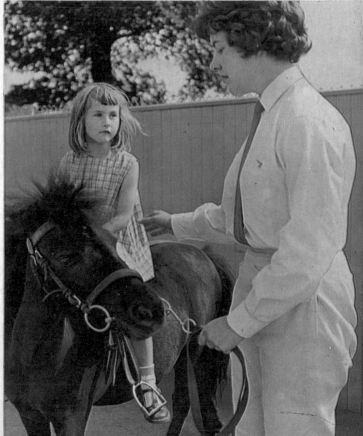

PLANT DESIGNER

How's this for a really unusual job for a girl? If you take it up, you'll probably be the only girl on the building site! For the plant we're talking about has nothing whatsoever to do with green fingers! It needs stone, brick, steel and cement.

Can you imagine yourself designing a complicated gas cooling tower, drawing it in detail, examining the soil on the site, surveying with a theodolite and supervising the whole building operation?

A job for a girl with a bright, clear brain!

Dear Diana Readers — You are invited to attend our gala performance. Admission is free. Just sit back, relax and turn the pages to enjoy the magic of ballet and ballerinas — prepared specially for You!

Wish Upon A Star

DIANNE RICHARDS
AS THE
"SUGAR PLUM FAIRY"

I love her dainty
  figure
Adore her simple
  grace
And the little smile
  of happiness
That lights her lovely
  face.
I love each perfect
  movement
As she twinkles on
  her toes
I love her gracious
  manner
Everywhere she goes
This is my wish. I
  want to be
A star as wonderful
  as she.

PRINCES AND PRINCESSES in Ballet

Princess Aurora is being danced here by Jane Landon.

The most famous Princess in ballet—Princess Aurora—appears in the great ballet THE SLEEPING BEAUTY.

To the music of Tchaikovsky, the ballet tells the story of the beautiful bewitched Princess doomed to sleep for a hundred years until she is awakened by the kiss of Prince Charming.

The ballet ends happily with the wedding of the Prince and Princess.

Stars of the Bolshoi Ballet dance in THE SLEEPING BEAUTY— Maya Plisetskaya in the role of the Princess and Maris Leipa as Prince Charming.

An important role in the famous ballet THE NUTCRACKER, is played by the handsome Prince, transformed by magic from the shape of a nut-cracker given to a young girl, Clara, as a Christmas present. In this wonderful ballet, set to Tchaikovsky's lovely music, the Prince transports Clara on a Magic journey to the Kingdom of Sweets, where they meet, among other fascinating characters, the Sugar Plum Fairy.

In this Festival Ballet presentation of THE NUTCRACKER, John Gilpin dances the part of the Prince, while Mary Williams plays the part of the little girl, Clara.

Here Karl Musil is the Prince, dancing with Irina Borowska in the role of the Sugar Plum Fairy.

In this Festival Ballet production, Doreen Wells dances the part of Odette.

The great classical ballet SWAN LAKE tells the tragic story of Prince Siegfried who falls in love with the beautiful Princess Odette, the victim of a wicked magician and doomed to take the form of a swan during the daylight hours. The unhappy Prince, trying to save Odette, is foiled by the magician's daughter, Odile.

Irina Borowska and Karl Musil dance the parts of Odile and Prince Siegfried.

A famous Prince in ballet appears in the ballet of the age-old fairytale CINDERELLA. Prima ballerina, Margot Fonteyn, made this story of the poor kitchen maid who became a Princess, one of her most famous roles.

Cinderella and the Prince, danced by Margot Fonteyn and David Blair.

Another version of CINDERELLA, with Svetlana Beriosova, partnered by Donald Macleary.

LUCKY PENNY MEETS LUCKY MASCOTS

BACKSTAGE IN BALLET

What a thrill it was meeting members of the Royal Ballet Touring Company. When I went backstage to meet some of the dancers, they were rehearsing " The Dream," at Oxford. Doreen Wells was dancing Titania, Queen of the Fairies, and David Wall was Oberon, the Fairy King.

Susan Lowe, Sheron Koshley, and Gail Thomas shared one enormous dressing-room with thirty other dancers, so it was a real race getting their news and views before their afternoon ballet classes.

First, I spoke to SUE LOWE, who dances the part of a dainty fairy in " The Dream."

heights you reach, you're always learning new steps or dances, or preparing for a new ballet. And you're always aiming to better your last performance—so, really, the sky is our limit, and I love trying to reach the impossible.

Then I turned to Gail Thomas—another Will-o'-the-Wisp Fairy in " The Dream."

Sue Lowe

Sheron Koshlev

Gail Thomas

What are your favourite colours ?

All pastel shades—except green, so many say that colour's unlucky.

How many pairs of ballet shoes do you use a week ?

It's difficult to say exactly—it rather depends on how frequently and strenuously the " pointes " are used. But usually about three pairs can last a week if we stitch and sew the satin " pointes " every day.

Which leading role would you most like to dance ?

Lise in " La Fille Mal Gardee " —that role suits my style of dancing. " La Fille Mal Gardee " also is my ideal of a perfect ballet.

Did you always dream of being a dancer ?

No, I didn't—I just seemed to fall into it. I took ballet lessons for fun when I was a little girl. When I was eleven years old, I was accepted for the Royal Ballet School —White Lodge, in Richmond, and once I started training there I changed very quickly and never wanted to stop dancing. I stayed at White Lodge for five years and then graduated to the senior school at Baron's Court, London—for another two years. When I left there, I came straight into the Royal Ballet Touring Company and joined the " Corps."

Then it was the turn of Sheron Koshley, who'd been Helena in " The Dream," to answer my questions.

If you could treat yourself to one thing—what would it be at this moment ?

Well, I'm car-mad—so my treat would be a WHITE Jaguar—only a white one.

If you weren't a ballet dancer —what would you like to be instead ?

I'd like to be married and have children. But if I had to work—I'd like to be a fashion model.

What do you think are the most necessary qualities needed to become a ballet dancer ?

There are a number of things. Good health. Endurance. A lot of perseverance—sometimes you have to go on, and on, and on, for hours, even days, practising just one step to get it perfect. But I think perhaps the most important thing is tremendous dedication and a genuine love of dancing — because almost your whole life is spent at classes, or rehearsals, or giving a performance. Of course, to be a really outstanding ballerina — you need " The Special Quality "—and you can only find out if you have " Star Quality " as you go along.

Why did you choose to become a ballet dancer ?

As far back as I can remember, I've always loved the ballet and enjoyed dancing. I've found it so satisfying and creative. In many other professions and careers, there's a limit to how far you can go—but not with the ballet— you've always something to look forward to. Whatever wonderful

What are some of your likes ?

Money. Perfume. Antiques. Lying in the sun. Swimming. Children— I've a soft spot for little boys of three to four years old. All accessories—gloves, scarves, shoes, &c. Avocado Pears. Audrey Hepburn. Paul Newman. Going to the cinema.

Which ballet do you most like to watch ? And which role would you most like to dance ?

I love watching the all-white ballet, " La Bayadere "—it's so beautiful and feminine. The role I'd like to dance—if I was given the choice and chance—is the girl in " Les Deux Pigeons."

Which leading role — out of the many ballets performed — do you think is the most difficult ?

Some think " Giselle," and others think " The Sleeping Beauty." But I'd say " Swan Lake " every time. It's such a long ballet and so hazardous to dance. The steps and sequences are incredibly intricate and need absolute precision and perfect timing from the ballerina. You also need a fantastic amount of stamina as you're on-stage nearly the whole time.

As a dancer of the Royal Ballet Company, could you describe a typical day ?

We start the morning with a limbering-up class for one and a half hours. After this, we put on stage make-up and costumes for the dress rehearsals—which begin at ten-thirty and finish at one o'clock. Then there's an hour's break to take off make-up and costumes and have a quick snack. The afternoons usually start with a short practice lesson, and afterwards—if we're not needed, we're free for a couple of hours—but most days we're called back onstage to go through various points noticed at the morning's rehearsals. By the time we've finished, there's only a short while left before we prepare for the evening performance and dance for another three hours.

I waved good-bye to the girls of the Corps de Ballet and wended my way along miles of corridor lined with gorgeous costumes hung in the spacious passages so that they won't get crushed or crumpled in the busy dressing-rooms—until I reached the dressing-room of Shirley Graham, one of the company's leading ballerinas.

Shirley was relaxing on a couch when I went in to chat to her.

Shirley
Graham

What is your height and weight ? Does a dancer have to be any special weight ?

My height is 5 ft. 3 in., and I weigh 7 st. 6 lb. But I don't think a ballet dancer has to be any special weight. Although, it's far easier to do the steps, especially the "Saute" and "lifts"—if you're slightly underweight.

Which ballet do you most enjoy dancing ?

Most certainly "Swan Lake"—it's a ballet I can really get hold of. There's plenty of scope for acting and dancing as the dual character, Odette and Odile. There's also a wonderful opportunity to express oneself and show one's abilities as a dancer. I've performed this role a number of times—and I must admit that, technically, it's terribly, terribly difficult, and it taxes my energy and strength to the absolute limit—but it will always be the loveliest ballet to me and the most satisfying to dance.

As one of the leading ballerinas —what is your great difficulty ? And which step do you find most difficult to do ?

My greatest difficulty is giving a performance when I'm not feeling on top of the world. We all try to do our very best before an audience, they're not expected to be interested in your aches and pains. But when I'm tired, or strained, or something's wrong somewhere—it's an effort to dance at all, let alone give a good performance. And the one step I dread doing are pirouettes—they terrify me,

Many people who work in the theatre carry a mascot with them for luck and these four dancers of the Royal Ballet Touring Company are no exception.

I asked SUE LOWE about her mascot, a sweet little donkey.

"It's just called The Donkey," said Sue, "it hasn't any other name.

"My donkey's very young, only five months old. Someone gave him to me at the beginning of this tour when I stepped out of line" for the first time and danced in "Pas de Six" from 'Swan Lake.'

"Does it bring me luck ? Well, I'm not superstitious and I don't believe that my donkey or any other mascot can make any difference to my having good or bad luck. I think it's a very different kind of luck that changes you or your career or your life."

SHERON KOSHLEY'S mascot is a funny little creature called Arthur the Gonk.

"It's Arthur's birthday today," Sheron told me, "he's one-year-old.

"Arthur was made for me by a dresser at Covent Garden. What I love about him is his goofy expression and funny face. Each time I see those saucer-like eyes—no matter how nervous or upset I feel—I always chuckle and cheer up.

"He stays at the theatre all the time, because I'm touring for six months of the year and if I left him at home I'd hardly ever see him. Arthur's become so much part of

my life it would be a real tussle to let my gonk go !"

Next it was the turn of GAIL THOMAS to tell me all about the mascot in her life—a cute little horse-figure called Pegasus.

"Pegasus was a parting gift from my teacher in New Zealand, five years ago, when I left for England," Gail began. "He's so tiny I always keep him in my make-up box for safety.

"Mascots are very personal and very much part of your own personality. Pegasus hasn't moved from this make-up box since he was given to me—but since this is a very special occasion—I'll let him loose just this once to be photographed."

Ballerina SHIRLEY GRAHAM'S mascot is a cuddly little kitten, which sits on her dressing-table at the mirror.

"My kitten was given to me by a friend at Covent Garden," said this lovely dancer, "when I danced my first solo role in 'Pas de Trois' in 'Swan Lake.'"

"I don't know whether this mascot has brought good luck, but cats and kittens are associated with pleasant events—and that's a comforting thought.

"This kitten is certainly my favourite companion and a marvellous listener. I can tell her all sorts of secrets. I'm very rarely without my mascot and at home she has a cosy spot to sit on at the window sill."

Portrait of a Ballerina

CLICK! The high-speed camera takes another picture of a pretty dancer. Come behind the scenes in a well-known London photographer's studio and see just what is involved and how much patience and skill is required. The photographer is Antony Crickmay.

At the appointed time, the young ballerina arrives at the studio. She is Jennifer Penney, of the Royal Ballet, and the role she is preparing for is Bluebird pas-de-deux in "Sleeping Beauty".

Tony's assistant arranges an appointment with a ballerina for the photographic session and plans the costume.

Jennifer changes into her costume and then proceeds with her special make-up. It needs concentration and skill to put this on properly.

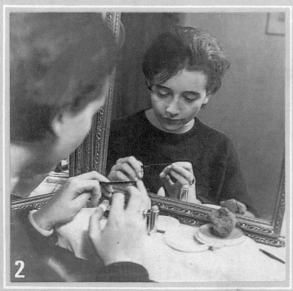

Specially heavy make-up for stage and photography is needed and this is all left out ready for the ballerina to put on.

The ballerina does her hair in the classical manner—

—and fixes on her headdress—

At last, the photographer is satisfied that everything is just right. The dancer takes up her position—the camera clicks—

Carefully, Jennifer binds on her shoes to complete the finishing touches to her costume.

—and this exciting and beautiful photograph is the result of all this hard work.

Tony has prepared the studio and makes a final check on the dancer's costume before the pictures are taken. Strong lighting is necessary in the studio for photographing ballet.

POP STARS

THE MAKING OF THE FILM

During the making of the film, Virginia McKenna, who plays the part of Joy Adamson, experienced the same kind of relationship with the lion cubs. This prompted her to write her book, "Playing With Lions," in which she tells the story of the making of the film.

Three lionesses played Elsa at different stages in the filming of her life. All the lions selected for the leading parts in "Born Free" were of the semi-wild type. Many had been rescued as abandoned cubs in the Kenya wilds, then given temporary shelter in some park or animal home. The parts of the three cubs at the very beginning of the film were played by Little Elsa, Spotty and Big Boy.

One night, Tomtom Tom, an enormous, black-maned lion, climbed the fourteen-foot high galvanised wire side of his enclosure. Only a terrified last-minute scream from an African sentry, which caused him to lose his footing, prevented a getaway.

What makes the film more exciting is the fact that Elsa's story is true. It is most extraordinary for a lioness to show such affection to humans — but Elsa was no ordinary lioness.

BORN FREE

The story of the film starring Virginia McKenna and Bill Travers

"Born Free," chosen to have its world premiere at the 1966 Royal Film Performance, is a best seller in 22 languages, and is one of the few "classic" books of modern times. It tells the true and heart-warming story of Elsa, one of three lion cubs reared by George and Joy Adamson after Mr Adamson had shot their parents out in the African veldt.

The task of feeding the starving cubs seemed almost impossible at first, as they were only a few days old and had been dependent on their mother for food. At last, through patience and perseverence, the Adamsons finally succeeded in feeding them milk—through a baby's bottle.

Day by day, the cubs grew stronger and when it was evident they would have to leave the Adamsons' compound, it was decided to send them to a zoo, but Mrs Adamson couldn't bear the thought of parting from Elsa, to whom she had become very attached. Almost at the last minute, George Adamson had a change of heart and decided to keep Elsa.

The Adamsons realised that Elsa could not stay with them for ever, as it would be cruel to deny her the life for which she was intended. As she had been brought up almost as a domestic pet, Elsa didn't know how to kill—and, once in the wild, her very survival would depend on her ability to kill. George Adamson undertook the task of teaching Elsa, and spent many hours showing her how to stalk and kill.

And then one day the inevitable happened. Elsa had a successful fight with another lioness and thus gained a place in a "pride." Although accepted by her own kind, faithful Elsa never forgot the Adamsons. Some time after, she returned to the compound complete with cubs, to introduce them, as it were, to her "foster parents."

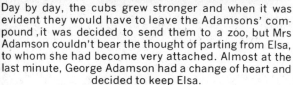